This is it!

NO-HOLDS-BARRED NOVEL THAT TELLS IT ALL
ABOUT SEX AND POWER IN WASHINGTON

*The
Washington
Fringe Benefit*

*The
Washington
Fringe Benefit*

The
Washington
Fringe Benefit

A NOVEL BY
ELIZABETH L. RAY

A DELL BOOK

Published by
Dell Publishing Co., Inc.
1 Dag Hammarskjold Plaza
New York, New York 10017

Dell ® TM 681510, Dell Publishing Co., Inc.

Printed in the United States of America

First printing—June 1976

In memory of my grandmother,
Della Smith Allen,
and all my doctors,
who have helped me through
my difficulties and distress.

Contents

The
Washington
Fringe Benefit

1
The Bureau of
Erotic Affairs

"Office of protocol" was the way I answered the phone that Sunday afternoon, but nothing could have been further from the truth. To begin with, it was a weekend, so I was at home, but even if I'd been in my plushey appointed office on Capitol Hill, I could hardly say my duties were concerned with protocol.

In three years as a highly paid secretary for the United States government, despite my respectable cover, I was actually a political fringe benefit, and if my department were to have a name, it would have been called the Bureau of Erotic Affairs.

On this particular gorgeous Sunday afternoon, I was in the middle of giving a bridal shower for a group of Hill secretaries. We were indulging in the popular Washington pastime of trading racy rumors about starchy public officials, and I was in a playful mood.

Suddenly, one of my girl friends began giving me a

sisterly lecture on my lack of formality around the Hill. She disapproved of the familiar way I addressed "the men who run our country" by their first names, buzzed around the Senate and House chambers as though they were social clubs, and used the official Capitol Hill telephone directory as my personal black book.

"Your trouble is, you don't understand the meaning of protocol," she was saying when the telephone rang.

On the spur of the moment, I picked up the phone in the kitchen and answered it, "Office of Protocol."

"Uh, I'm sorry, I must have the wrong number," the caller said, then hung up. When my "hotline" rang a moment later, I answered promptly.

"Hello, Elizabeth," the same voice volunteered guardedly. "This is your dentist calling . . ."

"My dentist?" I had dated several dentists, but this didn't sound like any of them.

"Yes, your oral surgeon. Don't you remember me?"

Again, I was stymied. I was beginning to think I'd heard his voice before, but not from the lips of my oral surgeon, whom I hadn't seen since a fund-raising dinner the previous week. And then, it hit me, and when it did, my legs went weak with excitement. The keynote speaker of the star-studded fund-raising dinner had been the legendary Senator Sincere. A man of unquestioned honesty, a respected family man, as well as a longtime Presidential hopeful, Senator Sincere had been a major figure in his party for almost as long as I could remember. When I'd run into him around the Hill or seen him on television, I had fantasized going to bed with him because he was such an important and distinguished man. Well, tonight was my chance. As luck

would have it, my escort, the oral surgeon, was a friend
of the Senator's, and was glad to make the introduction.
I looked really great, and I could tell Senator Sincere
wanted to get to know me, so I passed him my telephone number. We had met through our mutual dentist.
Dentist! That was it!

"Why, hello, Doctor," I murmered sultrily. "How are
you doing?"

"I'm fine, just fine," he said in his unmistakable,
raspy voice. "I just drove by your house on the way
back from dropping my wife at the airport."

Just like all the others, he had bundled his wife back
to their home state early, and was looking for a little
action before joining her when the Congress recessed for
summer later that week.

"What a pity you didn't drop by," I said, knowing I
would have gladly pushed my guests through a window
if he had. "Would you like to come over for a drink
now?"

"Well, thank you, but I'm home now," he said. "I
have to be on the Senate floor in the morning, and I
have some reading to catch up on beforehand. But how
about coming over here?"

"I'd love to." I tried to sound calm and casual, although I'm sure I didn't.

I was both flattered and surprised that the Senator
would take the risk of inviting me to his home. A lot of
guys with much less important reputations were even
nervous about coming to my place, but the Senator had
been around Washington long enough to know the ins
and outs of secret meetings, and he presented me with
the game plan for the evening. I was to announce my-

self to the gateman as Miss Pearl, who'd come to pick up Sincere's dentist friend "Dr. Driller." Once he made sure I had the strategy down, he said he couldn't wait for me to get there, and rang off.

I showered hurriedly, and dressed in a tight blue sweater and sleek white satin pants. Saying a hurried good-bye to my guests, I dashed downstairs, hopped into my sportscar, put the top down, and took off, my long platinum hair blowing in the breeze.

I could hardly believe I was on my way to the home of Senator Sincere. In many ways, it marked the realization of a longtime dream. When I first came to Washington, a wide-eyed girl from the farm, the powerful politicians had been no less than gods to me, and I couldn't imagine them doing mortal things like eating, sleeping, and making love until I started doing all of that with them.

Now I had made it into the home of one of the most important men in the country, and it was almost too much to comprehend. The fact he wanted me for my body didn't disturb me because, through him, I was moving in closer to the small circle of big people who ran everything.

That's the way it is in Washington, where everyone has their own method of scaling the ladder of influence. That my method was horizontal didn't make me less than many others, only different. I always made sure of that.

One time, I received a call from the aide of a Congressman who said, "A married friend of mine"—meaning his boss—"would like to have an appointment with you."

"What sort of appointment does he want?"

"Well, surely you know," he said coldly.

"Listen," I exploded, "how dare you call me up like that. I am not a hooker. I am an employee of the United States government."

The truth is, while I existed on the Congressional payroll strictly to date public officials in exchange for political favors, I did my job in high Washington style. Through that I earned entry into the Hill club, which meant that things had to be conducted through the proper channels.

Soon after I started work on Capitol Hill, I discovered that you couldn't operate without connections. While working as a temporary receptionist in a Congressman's office, I used to deal with applicants who walked in looking for jobs.

I'd check the résumé and stare at the person, amazed at how highly qualified they were, often with Yale or Harvard educations. But, as soon as they walked out, I was to throw the application into the waste-paper basket. "We hire only through personal contacts," I was told. If you're not connected in Washington, if you don't have "the juice," you're nowhere.

For me, and for a lot of other people, the closer to the White House you can get, the more important you are, and Senator Sincere was among the closest to the White House. Being with him would be the sexual coup of my career.

Dusk was settling in as I arrived at Sincere's stately apartment building in Washington, and drove up to the stern-faced security guard. "My name is Miss Pearl," I announced, "and I'm here to meet Dr. Driller, who's visiting Senator Sincere."

The guard scanned the tenant list. "Right," he said. "You're down here. Proceed, park over there, and take elevator H." If he suspected anything, he didn't show it.

The building was very elegant, with richly decorated hallways, thick carpet, and chandeliers, and I started getting nervous as I walked toward the formidable door and pressed the buzzer. It took the longest second of my life until the door opened, and I saw him standing there.

Senator Sincere, who looked just like his pictures, was dressed in plaid slacks and a Burning Tree Golf Club T-shirt. "Hi," he said in his customary, cordial style, then hurried me inside and out of sight. "Nice to see you."

He offered me a light gin and tonic, which I needed, because, face to face with my fantasy encounter, I was suddenly uncomfortable. I think he was uncomfortable, too, and as we sat down on the floral-patterned sofa, we both had a little trouble starting up a conversation.

Senator Sincere wasn't telling any secrets that evening, but he did try to make small talk, which I felt was very gracious of him. He quickly got on the subject of my life and asked me what my ambitions were. I told him my dream was to go to Hollywood, enroll in acting school, and, hopefully, make it as a leading actress.

"Let me know when you do," he said warmly, gazing into my eyes, "and I'll give you some names." We'd only been together for a few minutes, and already he was giving me contacts. I have rarely felt so flattered.

To my surprise, Sincere started showing me pictures

of his wife, kids, and of his big, beautiful house in his hometown, complete with swimming pool and well-tended grounds. I couldn't understand why he was showing me those photos; maybe guilt nudged him.

We got through the family album pretty fast, and then he asked me if I would like to see the rest of the apartment. "After I finish my drink," I said, since I had only had a couple of sips.

"Bring it with you," he replied as he helped me up, taking my arm.

The Senator led me casually from the living room through the library and the dining room, but as soon as we got to the bedroom, he grabbed me and started kissing me.

"Excuse me a moment." I drew away and walked into the bathroom. I had to pinch myself to prove I was not dreaming when I spotted all those beautiful towels bearing the famous monogram. Amidst this fantasy come true, I undressed slowly, pulled a monogrammed towel off a rack, and wrapped it around me. When I came out, the Senator was waiting for me in bed.

"My God, what a gorgeous body you have," he exclaimed, as my towel dropped to the carpet.

I walked over to him, and as I kissed him, I pulled back the blankets and let my hand roam over his body. He was breathing heavily as the tip of my tongue ran around the rim of his ear, plunged inside it, moved to his neck, and down his chest. I sucked his nipples, biting just a little, which really excited him.

Slowly, I worked my way down over his stomach and groin, and nibbled at his balls before taking his cock in my mouth. He was almost choking with ecstasy, and I was excited, too, but for different reasons.

As his cock pumped deeper and deeper down my throat, I was struck by the idea that, at that moment, all his power rested in me. I may never go down in history, I couldn't help thinking, but I am certainly going down *on* it. All too soon, he began panting that he was going to come. "You've got me so excited, I can't wait," he gasped, and shot off into my mouth.

Once the Senator's lust was gratified, he became very time-conscious. "Gee, Liz," he said before he was even up off the bed, "it must be getting quite late. They're going to be wondering downstairs what's keeping you."

I knew he was desperate to get me out of there, but that was fine, because both of us had gotten what we wanted out of the encounter. He'd had sex, and I'd had power, plus a special added attraction, the knowledge that I'd been with one of Washington's most powerful politicians.

After I dressed, Sincere gave me a set of instructions for sneaking past the security guard so complicated that the CIA would have been baffled. He asked me to repeat the plan back to him a couple of times to make sure it sank in. "I've got it," I assured him. "Left, then right, then straight through the unmarked exit."

However, on the elevator ride down, I began to resent the fact that, once the intimacy started, the chivalry ended, and by the time I reached my car, I was really fuming.

I jumped into my car, started the motor, and turned right. "Hi," I said to the same guard who admitted me earlier as "Miss Pearl." "I'm Elizabeth Ray, and I don't remember whether Senator Sincere told me to go left or right for Memorial Bridge."

"This way, ma'am," he replied, unable to suppress a smile, and neither could I.

2
More Perfect Unions

I was registered, twenty-seven years ago, into this world electorate minus one basic human right—someone to want me. Robbie, my mother, didn't. To her I was the living reminder of a roll in the hay.

My father didn't, although, to be fair, I don't think anyone ever polled him on the subject, possibly because nobody, least of all me, could identify him.

Only my beloved grandma told me I was a pretty child. Everyone else thought I was funny-looking, and, although it was the truth, it hurt. I had enormous blue eyes, limbs like matchsticks, and a shape to match, but even back then, I vowed I would emerge one day into a butterfly.

Robbie, as she liked to be called, was utterly untamed, despite grandmother's efforts to civilize her. She could always find a way to sneak off, and when I was a little girl I remember often being left alone while she would rendezvous with her latest beau. Usually I found myself being cared for by others.

Of all the eleven offspring my hardworking grandmother tried to raise outside the sleepy town of Marshall, North Carolina, Robbie was her biggest letdown. All grandma could do was increase her vigilance and pray for all our sakes that my mother would start bringing some financial support into the house. But when Robbie did almost make some money, I was nearly lost in the process.

Robbie's scheme involved shipping me off to an uncle, who had moved to Pittsburgh. The entire family agreed this was a good thing and was disappointed when the deal fell through, because Robbie had demanded certain conditions which my uncle wouldn't agree to.

Things changed when my relatives decided that Robbie should get married. They knew it wouldn't be easy to find a husband, so they were all thrilled when an uncle dragged home some poor old millworker, named Henry. He was over six feet tall, with a mean country face, bug eyes, huge ears, and a mouthful of yellowing teeth. To my mother, though, Henry was Adonis, and to the others he was nothing short of Lord Bountiful.

Not only did he actually own a motorcar, something we rarely saw, let alone rode in, but to prove he could provide for Robbie, he brought lots of food when he came to call. That clinched it. My Robbie was about to be made an honest woman, like it or not.

After the nuptials, the couple moved into their honeymoon palace, which was a log cabin no bigger than two Congressional telephone booths, about five miles out of town on the edge of French Broad River. Tiny though it was, her new house was as impressive to Robbie as if it were the Governor's own mansion. And, most importantly, she felt she had achieved respectability as a married lady.

The day came when Robbie decided to test her new status, so into town we went, straight to the local haberdasher. I felt like a little princess in my new two-dollar yellow dress, and after we paraded me around town, we boarded the bus back to the log cabin to show me off to the bridegroom.

Henry was chopping wood when he arrived, and was not very impressed with my new outfit. To demonstrate his point, he chased us out of the place, brandishing his ax. "You're not buying clothes for someone else's child with my money," he hollered. "Whore! Off-bred!"

Robbie and I ran out of there like scalded coyotes, screaming so loud you could have heard us all the way to Raleigh, and we didn't look back until we reached a neighbor's place two miles away. We were offered refuge in her barn for the night, but we were afraid to sleep for fear Henry might sniff us out like a couple of moles.

Next morning, when I was still alive, I really believed it must have been through the will of God, and when Henry appeared relatively calm, to claim us, I began to feel things would improve. But on the reckless car ride home, when the door of the vehicle flew open, I nearly fell out. I don't think it would have mattered to Henry. I was so afraid of this ignorant clod that I rarely went to visit Robbie.

Now that the kinfolk had drifted off, I was living alone with grandma. Times were lean, and grandmother and I were left to fend for ourselves on her thin welfare check. For all our deprivation, mama, as I now called her, managed to keep the house and ourselves spotlessly clean. The few clothes I owned were kneaded almost threadbare against the scrubboard inside a tin tub, so the cruel kids at school couldn't say I was not clean. It was bad enough that they rejected me because of my origins. To the good people of Marshall, Robbie was a living legend, all right.

Although I enrolled a year late in Marshall Junior High School, I worked hard and made decent grades. There was nothing to do but work, since nobody would be my friend. As I grew older and more aware, I told myself that one day I'd make myself a success.

In my last year of junior high school, one of my uncles presented mama with a scheme for selling our ramshackle property and, with the proceeds, buying a nicer house, closer to town, where she and I and the uncle's new wife would live.

By now, mama's health had started to falter. It was obvious that a young girl and a frail old lady needed help, so my uncle and aunt installed us in an electric blue trailer alongside their Asheville home.

The dream house was not to be, but even the trailer was luxurious to me. For the first time in our lives, mama and I had two modern conveniences: indoor plumbing and TV. I'd never even heard of television before, and now my eyes were open to a world I'd never dreamed of. Elvis Presley had been a poor kid like myself. Gale Storm became American womanhood, and Johnny Carson in "Who Do You Trust?" was a hero.

What with my good school marks and my wonderful new fantasies, I was convinced that only good things lay ahead. But one afternoon, during my junior year of high school, I came home to find mama had been taken to the hospital. I cried in fear and sorrow, for selfish as well as sentimental reasons. While I loved her dearly, I knew that if she died, I would be at the mercy of my relatives until I graduated from school and severed my family ties.

Grandmother always said she had three important missions in life. One was to make sure the kinfolk didn't foreclose on their threat to send me to an orphan's home, another was to prevent my falling into my mother's ways, and the third was to live long enough to see me happily married.

"I hope you find someone to love you as I do, little Betty Lou," she used to say, as she fastened the last rubber band on my platinum pigtail. "You deserve it."

By my early teens, my slender frame had ripened to eye-pleasing voluptuousness. I enjoyed the boys' stares, because for the first time, I was actually getting attention. I was glad I looked like Robbie, but the last thing in the world I wanted was to end up like her.

That summer before graduation, I made a swift transition from childhood to awakening adulthood. I identified with popular songs that blared out from car radios, and Bobby Rydell's "Wild One [I'm Gonna Tame You Down]" was written just for the irresistible Jezebel I was going to be. I even composed a country song called "Will He Need Me?"

As I looked at myself in the mirror in my short shorts and drawstring blouses, experimenting with cerise lipstick from W. T. Grant's, I wondered if I would ever grow up to be like the actresses I was seeing at the Biltmore Drive-In for the first time that summer.

My steady escort was a man named Tank Dawson, who was too old for me, which made him exciting. He would call for me in his pickup truck, and off we'd go to the dreamworld of the movies.

Technicolor females like Sandra Dee and Tuesday Weld were enviable creatures from another world to me, but the magnificent Marilyn Monroe was my idol. I worshiped her, devoured every breathless item in the fan magazines, and sat through every one of her movies three times with Tank Dawson.

After the movies, we would drive over to Marshall schoolyard for some innocent necking, but no more. Tank Dawson had always been a perfect gentleman and I believed there was no reason to be afraid.

No reason, that is, until the night I saw the gleam of a mean-looking knife at my neck and realized Tank was unhinged by the opportunity available to him at ten o'clock in the deserted schoolyard. He ordered me to remove my shorts and forced his way into me with the savagery of an animal. Believing this act had condemmed me to an early motherhood was almost as bad as the searing pain and the sight of blood on my thighs.

"You've made me pregnant," I cried, sure I was already stuck with my first illegitimate child, but before he could answer, there was a flash of headlights, and a police car passed by. "Stop that crying, get dressed, and don't you say a word," he ordered, tucking the knife inside his leather jacket.

As soon as the car drove off, I started wailing again. "All right," he said, "I'll marry you."

What a way to end my life before it had a chance to begin, I thought, as we sped through the night across the state border to Spartanburg, South Carolina, looking for a justice of the peace. It was early morning when we arrived there, however, and the whole town was asleep.

We drove around for a while, I inconsolable and he unremorseful but promising we'd tell our folks we had fallen in love and wanted to get married the next day.

When we got home, my aunt and uncle were waiting for us, along with a very pregnant woman who said she was Tank's wife and who proceeded to break a Coke bottle over his head. Embarrassing though it was, I confessed everything to my aunt, who became determined to find me a safe and suitable husband.

Around graduation time, I had started dating what to my aunt was a perfect catch, Joey Jones, a local boy. Joey firmly believed a woman's place is in the home, and that mothering is her job. He also disapproved strenuously of women driving cars and smoking cigarettes. He was the horniest, pimpliest, palest boy in town, but our relationship blossomed into an engagement and the wedding was planned for the summer after I was graduated. The family even looked the other way when they caught us necking in Joey's car before Sunday school class.

My unsuspecting grandmother, now home from the

hospital, was sleeping serenely in the next room when, one night, Joey produced his penis and asked me to suck it. I refused, but because he was so persistent, I touched it and watched him ejaculate into his handkerchief. The next night, he was back with a crumpled pack of rubbers, insisting we go all the way. I consented, but he was dreary and unromantic, and I didn't enjoy it at all.

My wedding day dawned a bright fall Saturday, with sixty beaming people in attendance. I wore a sweet, white coat and dress outfit, my hair was in simple curls, and I carried a small, gold-embossed Bible and a delicate spray of lily of the valley.

The organ played "Oh Promise Me" as I walked slowly down the aisle, watching the happy faces of the folks and thinking about my future with Joey.

Somehow, I realized, I had accelerated too fast from girlhood to womanhood and was missing the experience of knowing life. There just had to be more to it than Joey Jones.

Halfway down the aisle, I spotted a door, open and inviting, and suddenly I found myself running through it. I didn't stop until I reached my rented room in Asheville and flushed my diamond engagement ring down the toilet, aghast at what I had done, and glad I had done it.

3
Discover America

After my sudden escape from the church and a life of anonymity as Mrs. Joey Jones, I was definitely convinced marriage was not for me.

If a man started getting too close, I just had to pick up and move on, because I had no intention of settling down until I became somebody.

Now that I was on my own, I decided my only ambition in life was to be a movie actress. Work would be merely a source of money for acting classes, although it was possible that in a job, I would meet an influential man, hopefully a millionaire, who would take me under his wing and aid me with my career.

My first position was behind the candy counter at W. T. Grant's in Ashville, North Carolina. If a nice customer asked for a half pound of something, I'd dish out a couple of pounds, and if the customer was testy, I'd do the opposite. I'd like to think I had a little something to do with Grant's filing bankruptcy.

In no time, the profits in my section started to plunge, and the store manager ordered me out. However, a hand-horny section manager, Mr. Nestor, fought to keep me on because I let him brush up against my breasts every time he reached across to the cash register.

I was already discovering that I could count on my physical attributes to get me a job, or to keep me in one. Even later on, when I was giving out more than just a harmless feel, there was always one man who would keep me hanging in there when things got rocky.

However, once I realized that Mr. Nestor was the best I could do at Grant's, I took off. I was restless and impatient, and if a humdrum job did not instantly materialize into a golden opportunity, I went on to something else.

Sometimes I'd stay in a job as long as a month, and sometimes I stayed only till my first lunch hour, not even bothering to come back and pick up my paycheck. If the boss didn't encourage me to leave, job monotony did. As a result, I bounced in and out of no less than seventy jobs in three years.

From retailing, I moved on to banking, working first at the Wachovia Federal Bank, where I was hoping they'd put me out front among the wealthy customers.

Instead, I was put in the back room with the accounts. Even with an adding machine, I had difficulty making things balance, so I'd put the deposits in my drawer, intending to get back to them later when I had more time. Meanwhile, customers' checks started bouncing all over Asheville. People who'd deposited

$5,000 would find $20 checks rejected for insufficient funds, while others found themselves with hundreds of unexplained dollars in their accounts. And when I told the manager I was leaving to work at French Broad Bank down the street, he didn't stop me. Neither did the manager of French Broad when I said I was moving to First National. And so on.

Having exhausted banking, I decided to try communications and applied for a job as a telephone operator. At Southern Bell, I ended up on the long-distance night shift, which was so quiet I had to make phone calls to friends to keep myself awake. Pretty soon, the supervisor called me aside and cautioned me against placing private calls, but I became so bored that I began to liven things up by plugging astonished late-night callers into Dial-a-Prayer or the police department.

When complaint letters started pouring in, phone people advised me that I didn't have the aptitude for telephone work, which was fine by me because I wanted to be among people, where I'd be noticed.

Searching for a glamorous and exciting career, I decided to become a stewardess and applied to a regional airline called Piedmont. For the interview, I dressed in a demure gabardine suit and a prim white lace blouse, but the first thing the man asked me was to take off my jacket so he could see how I'd look in their uniform. At the end of the interview, the Piedmont personnel man asked me to meet him for dinner, but I refused, because I thought he was a little weird, so I didn't get the job. However, I was accepted by Eastern Airlines, who flew me to Miami for the six-week training course.

Almost as soon as I arrived, I met a good-looking

pilot named Sam, and within a couple of weeks, he was telling me he loved me and asking me to marry him. A week before graduation, he became so insistent that we had a horrible fight, which upset me so much I refused to go back to school.

I immediately regretted what I'd done, but having already burned my bridges, I had to move on. I didn't want to hang around Florida, and I couldn't return to Asheville without being successful. If I came back poor and obscure, they would say I was a failure like my mother, which was one thing I was determined not to be.

The only place I knew to run to was Washington D.C., which I had visited in my senior year at school. Even then, I had been awestruck by the magnificent Capitol buildings and the impressive historic monuments.

I only intended to stay in Washington until I had saved the money for acting school in Los Angeles or New York. Washington, it seemed to me, was a company town, where you had to be successful, rich, and powerful to survive. I never for a second imagined that Betty Lou Ray, fugitive from the wrong side of the tracks in Marshall, North Carolina, would become part of the life at the top, certainly not in the way that I did.

Having made it to our nation's capital, with twenty dollars and one suitcase to my name, I moved in with a girl friend from back home, and went straight out to look for a job.

My best prospect was the telephone company, but I had such terrible references from Southern Bell, I had to pretend I hadn't had any experience. The people at Southern Telephone were impressed by how quickly I caught on, and began assuring me I had a well-paid future as a chief operator.

I went to work in the Arlington office, and soon Gavin Kenney, who floated around the entire Washington district, came by the office and noticed me. He gave me a look, I gave him a look, and when I went outside on my coffee break, he was waiting to ask me for a date.

He was good-looking, and I thought he might even help me get promoted, so we had an affair, but when he started telling me he loved me, I got bored. Almost immediately after I dropped him, I met a traveling sales representative for IBM, named Albert Tasker. I used my position as an operator to call him long-distance in places like Dallas and Atlanta dozens of times a day. I was caught and cautioned, but when I kept it up, they fired me.

Even though I'd moved in with Albert, I had to have a job to feed and clothe myself, so the following week I went into the Washington office of Chesapeake and Potomac Telephone Company, and told them my name was Mrs. Betty Lou Tasker and that I had never before been employed as an operator.

When I heard they intended sending me to the Arlington office, from which I'd just been banished, I told them I had a sick husband in the District and had to be located closer to town. Yet my past was still to haunt me, as I discovered one day, soon after I started work, when the supervisor called me off the board.

"Mrs. Tasker," she said very formally, "I'd like you to meet Mr. Gavin Kenney. Mr. Kenney, this is our newest employee, Mrs. Betty Lou Tasker."

Kenney hadn't known I'd left Arlington, and his jaw

dropped in surprise, but fortunately, he kept his mouth shut. In fact, I lasted a couple of weeks, until one of the girls I worked with in Arlington was transferred to Central.

The supervisor called me in again, but this time, she was not wearing her cheery smile. "Miss Ray," she enunciated very clearly, "for reasons we do not wish to disclose, you are no longer employed with this company, nor will you be ever again in the future." And that was that.

After I left the phone company, I worked in and on the fringes of the travel industry, setting a rapid employment record, even for me. In the space of two weeks, I had jobs with Hertz, Avis, and National Car Rental. I was assigned to Washington National Airport, and I found walking around the arrival lounge and talking with passengers more stimulating than standing behind a counter, but I was being paid to do a desk job, so that didn't work out.

I had several travel reservations jobs, starting with the newly introduced auto-train, which was very popular and often overbooked. So I started bumping long-standing bookings off to give places to my friends. When the complaints came in, I was out.

It was very rare that I had a problem getting work since, in those days, it was men who usually did the hiring, and I made sure I got their full attention. I used to dress in form-fitting outfits, wore becoming makeup, and always kept my blond hair perfectly groomed.

After bowing out of the travel game, I tried interior decorating school, which I thought was going to be glamorous, colorful, and exciting; but when they sat me at a little desk with a T square and bunch of books and measurements, I saw it was no different from the accounts department at the Wachovia Bank, and away I went.

Following that, I took classes at the now defunct National Academy of Broadcasting in downtown Washington, where I was the only female in the class of seventeen students, all training to be disc jockeys. We learned how to operate a turntable, write and read news and commercial copy, and all about FCC rulings, and I attended every day from nine in the morning until three in the afternoon and worked diligently.

Once in a while, I would take a long lunch hour and forget to come back, but the teacher, who used to come by my place to help me with my homework, told me not to worry. As a result, I had an excellent attendance record, but didn't feel confident about passing the exams.

However, the grader who marked the papers and gave out the diplomas was a new friend of mine, and the night before graduation, I invited him over for dinner and sex. Next day, I became a qualified broadcaster with an impressive certificate complete with a gold seal, but when I found out the best starting salary a female broadcaster could expect was a miserable forty dollars a week, I pitched the certificate and moved on to the entertainment field.

I was hired as the cigarette girl at a nightclub called Top of the Town, which featured a spectacular view of the Washington Monument. I always wore eye-popping low-cut gowns, and I went over very big with the customers. Wearing a low-cut gown, I used to bend provocatively over the regulars and coo, "Let me light your

fire, sir," or "Isn't it a wonderful view from up here?"
As I was lighting their cigarette and they were checking
my cleavage, they'd quip, "It certainly is a wonderful
view!" To another guy, who reminded me of Colonel
Sanders, I'd say, "Hi, Colonel. What will it be tonight, a
breast or a leg?"

All the men would give me a little squeeze and a
large tip, sometimes paying for the whole tray of cigarettes, then giving it straight back for me to sell over
again. Everyone called me Betty Boobs and saw me as a
sexy version of Goldie Hawn. I even worked up a little
comedy routine and sang one or two songs.

Acting was still my big dream, but everyone would
tell me to forget it, saying I didn't have the background,
I should have started when I was younger—I was only
twenty-two at the time—my name was wrong, my nose
was too big. And as for my southern accent, it used to
send them into hysterics. Follow-through is not always
my strongest quality, but resourcefulness is, and I set
out to overcome my seemingly insurmountable problems.

First, I changed my name from basic Betty Lou to
sophisticated Elizabeth. My worst feature had always
been my nose, and I decided it was time to change that,
too. One night at work, a customer introduced me to a
friend of his, a plastic surgeon, whom I'll call Dr. Peel,
and I made an appointment to see him in his office.

At the time, I didn't have the money for a nose job,
but was pretty sure we could work something out, and
after that first appointment, I felt certain we could. The
doctor told me to undress so he could examine my body
for scars, and he was so impressed by seeing me nude

he told me the one thing I would never need changed was my anatomy. He said I had one of the most gorgeous bodies he'd ever seen, and started fondling my back, my buttocks, and my outer and inner thighs. He got up to my breasts, and started sucking them. "Good," he exclaimed, a while later, "you're going to heal just fine."

He asked me to have dinner with him that evening, and when he resumed the examination in my bedroom, I was sure the fee wouldn't be a problem.

In situations like this, I never feel used, because whenever someone does me a good turn in exchange for my favors, I feel I'm using their time, their skills and natural assets, just as they're using mine. I do not accept money from anyone. My arrangements, like the one with Dr. Peel, are merely fair exchanges.

On the evening before the operation, the good doctor came to my hospital room with a Polaroid camera and snapped pictures of my nose, for his record. Then he pulled down the top of my sexy, peach lace nightgown and snapped photos of my breasts.

I was sitting cross-legged on the edge of the bed facing him, not wearing any underpants. As he walked toward me, I could see he was already hard. Without worrying about the cataract patient in the next bed who, poor thing, had bandages over her eyes, Dr. Peel whipped out his cock and drew my head down toward it.

"Please insert this in your mouth, Miss Ray," he ordered me. "I want to check your temperature."

After about as long as it would have taken a thermometer to register, he started panting, but soon escalated to groans. The poor lady with the cataracts was concerned. "Is there anything wrong in the next bed?" she called out feebly.

It was a few moments before I was able to answer her. "Oh, nothing," I gasped. "The doctor just dropped his instrument."

Next morning, on the operating table under a local anesthetic, I could see Dr. Peel working away on me, but even in surgery, he was still mixing a little pleasure with business. "Just look at that," he was saying to the scrub nurse as he folded back my gown and showed her my naked body. "Have you ever seen anything as gorgeous?" Nothing's sacred, I thought, but I was too drugged to care; besides, I knew that when I got out of there, I was going to be a changed person.

Anatomy-obsessed as he was, Dr. Peel was a very gifted plastic surgeon, and I was really pleased with the cute new nose he gave me. It bolstered my confidence and encouraged me to resurrect my lifelong ambition to become an actress.

I was still working at all kinds of jobs around the place, struggling to save money for my acting lessons, but I was not sure I could also afford the voice lessons, which were quite expensive, but a necessary part of dramatic training. There had to be a way to afford them.

I knew of a man considered to be one of the finest coaches on the East Coast, who was located right in Washington. Although I knew I could never pay his prices, I went to see him and told him how I'd worked my way out of the South in pursuit of my acting goal. He listened sympathetically, then offered to see me on a once-a-week basis at irregular hours. I was flattered that so respected a teacher would make exceptions for me and accepted eagerly. All too soon, however, he began insisting that we hold the lessons at my apartment, and, since I didn't have a piano, it was all too clear what he was after, and I told him to go play his organ someplace else.

Discouraged by the wages of the worldly Washington life, I decided to seek spiritual comfort from the Church. Eager for religious instruction, I began studying with a priest.

Father, as I always called him, was in his mid-forties, with close-cropped salt and pepper hair and beard, distinguished looks, and a beautiful voice. Had he not been an untouchable man of the cloth, I could easily have fallen in love with him.

I attended my lessons, trying to learn and making some progress over the course of a year. Father was such a fine person that, after a while, he became to me a father, psychiatrist, and teacher all rolled into one, listening to my problems after classes, and lecturing me about the need for faith in my life.

He was so understanding and charming that I started having vivid fantasies about him. I was sad because I couldn't have him, and wrote him postcards whenever I went on a trip, inscribed, "I love you," which I did in every way. I used to ask him if we could possibly have dinner together, but he always declined. I'd ask him to please kiss me good-bye as I left, and he'd plant a harmless peck on my cheek and say, "Go with God, my child."

The relationship probably would have remained a pure influence in my life, had it not been for a rainy

Saturday afternoon when I urgently needed to speak to him. I was very depressed and felt he was the only person I had to turn to, so I called him.

He told me to come on over, and we sat in his library and talked for a while. Then he decided walking around would calm me down, and we went on a tour of the dining room and the living areas, and somehow, as we were getting to the boiler room, he talked of my need to embrace religion.

I was so crazy about this man that all I could think about was embracing him, although I knew it was an impossible dream. I looked into his face, and I knew he could read my mind, and suddenly he said, "Come here, my child," drawing me behind the boiler.

We started kissing, and I was so excited that I wanted to touch his cock, but he brushed my hand away. He continued to kiss my face, my neck, and my shoulders very passionately. "Take off your sweater and let me look at you," he urgently ordered me.

I was not wearing underwear, and he easily bent down and started sucking my breasts. I got so excited, I was just dripping wet, thinking how much I'd like to make love to him.

But then, as suddenly as he'd started caressing me, he stopped. We got dressed and went back upstairs, where he gave me a chaste good-night hug.

After that, fantasies of having him inside me were constantly in my mind, and one night, about a week after the first encounter, I called him and asked if I could come over. He must have been having sexy thoughts, too, because he urged me to come.

It was about eleven o'clock when I arrived at his

house, and he was waiting for me. There was nobody else around, and it was dark and silent inside the room he led me into. He kissed me, then went over and sat, uneasily, in a chair.

"Take off your clothes and let me see your gorgeous body," he said, removing his collar and jacket, which he did not wish to defile, since he was already violating vows he'd observed for twenty years.

When I was naked, I went over and kneeled down before him on the floor. He reached down and took my breasts in his hands and started squeezing them. I was aching to touch his penis, and this time he let me do it. I unzipped his pants and took his cock into my mouth. I could hardly wait to feel him inside of me, so I went slowly, not wanting him to come too fast, but he climaxed almost immediately. Ten minutes later, he was behaving as if it hadn't happened.

I continued to see him for instruction, but after a while, he told me he felt I was not ready to take Catholicism seriously, and we lost touch with each other, even though it was a long time before I could get him out of my mind.

By now, I was working as a hostess in the Watergate Hotel cocktail lounge, and I was sick of waiting on people. It was June 1972, and I was pretty depressed on the day when I happened to take a call for a girl who was no longer there.

"Pammy doesn't work here anymore, but if you give me your name," I said, "I'll pass on the message."

"My name is Elan Bright," the caller said in a peppy, friendly voice. I'd heard that Bright, a well-known oil lobbyist, was a real live wire around town, and I decided to prolong the conversation.

"Oh, this is Elizabeth Ray speaking," I said, "and you're just the person I want to talk to."

Thinking nothing would come of it, I told him I was looking for a job with a future, and I was surprised when he told me to come up to his office to see him.

Next evening, dressed in a while body shirt, hotpants, and white boots, I drove down to his office in my little red Volkswagen.

Bright turned out to be a roly-poly Texan in his late fifties with a good sense of humor and a talent for making people feel relaxed. I liked him on sight. He showed me to his plush office, and I could hardly believe my ears when he offered me a starting salary of $8,700 a year. That was more money than I'd had in my entire life, and a hell of a lot more than the $125 I was earning at the time, so I accepted immediately.

"But what do I have to do?" He had not mentioned anything about typing or other clerical skills.

"Just come in for the afternoon shift," he told me in his engaging, breezy manner, "and sit over there at that extra desk."

The following Monday, I joined political life, never dreaming that I would make the biggest impact on Capitol Hill since the British burned it down.

4

The Fringe Benefit

Elan Bright, as we'll call him, was a man who wore his name spectacularly well. One of the most flamboyant figures on the entire Hill, he entertained with exuberance.

"May we live as long as we want to, and want to as long as we live," and "The Lord giveth, the Lord taketh away" were his favorite sayings.

Lobbyist Bright was fun-loving and God-fearing at the same time, and when he said, "See you in church," he meant it, even if we had been into the most unholy mischief the night before. His enviable reputation for persuasion almost equaled his fame as the employer of the most gorgeous girls on Capitol Hill.

My first day on the job, I arrived wearing what was to be my uniform, tight sweaters and slacks or miniskirts, which raised not only a few office eyebrows, but some hackles as well.

Harriet, a pretty redhead who had until that day been the boss's pet, came over to my desk, plunked down an application form, and asked me to type it up! When I told her I had already been hired, she replied that the form was a requirement which everybody, no matter what his or her connections, must complete. "May I fill it out by hand?" I asked her.

"We prefer you use the typewriter," she archly responded.

When I admitted I didn't know how to type, she suggested my skills might be put to better use in a massage parlor and stalked off.

The other office girls were also resentful of my appearance, and began playing cruel tricks on me like unplugging the electric typewriter when I was trying my hardest to work, hiding the checkbooks, and inventing scurrilous stories about my morals and my competence. I had gotten what I wanted, but holding onto it would be something else again.

One of the terms of my employment was a thirty-day probationary period, and my boss himself subsequently confessed he was surprised I lasted because he was convinced I was not capable of handling the office work. I was determined and diligent, however, coming in early and working as hard as I could.

Two weeks after I was hired, I was called upon to do a little homework for my boss, who invited me for drinks at the Rotunda, a dimly lit downstairs bar-restaurant that's the House hangout.

Afterward, we went back to my apartment and balled. He was a pretty good lay and all, but I didn't let myself get carried away. Just like Bright's other encounters, his session with me was nothing more than a one-night stand. As a playboy, Bright liked variety, and as a family man, he wasn't interested in getting involved. As a businessman, he was just trying out the merchandise to see if it was top quality. No, we weren't destined to be the Romeo and Juliet of Capitol Hill. Lobbyist Bright had other plans for me.

My working hours in the office, noon to eight, were unusual for a Hill secretary, but compatible with Bright's. From five in the afternoon until eight at night, I manned the reception desk, answered the telephones, and occasionally typed up a two-line letter, which I mailed out with some booklet or other.

From noon to five, I was more like a Hill page, carrying mail or escorting constituents and other visitors over to the House floor when Bright was there. This was my favorite aspect of my job, because I was doing what I like best: walking around, meeting people, and being noticed.

My romps around the hallowed halls of Congress were lots of fun, and I began to be regarded as a sort of sexy mascot around the Capitol. When I wasn't actually hanging around the Capitol building, I used to tool around the Hill in my chocolate brown Corvette with the top pulled back, waving to everybody. Soon everyone knew whom I worked for and started greeting me like their own personal ray of sunshine. "Hi, Elizabeth," this or that congressman, the influential doormen of the chambers, or the uniformed security guards would say. "How's our girl today?" If I skipped a visit, they would tell me the next day how much they had missed seeing me.

I was frequently required to take a message to a congressman or senator when he was on the House or Senate floor. You do this by handing a note to the doorman, who passes it to the member or senator who, provided he sees fit, will come on out and speak to you.

Obviously, you should have an official, or at least relatively important, reason to drag him out in the middle of what may be a sensitive legislative or historic moment. However, I would often decide I wanted a word with someone in session, and, on the spur of the moment, I write a provocative little note and slip it to the doorman, who'd deliver it. In minutes, the man I'd want to see would come dashing out the door and say something like, "Hi, Elizabeth. What can I do for you today?"

"Oh, nothing," I'd say, swinging playfully around the tall arm of the wide timber staircase opposite the chamber doors. "I just wanted to see how you were, and say hello." They were always flattered by my thinking of them, more amused than annoyed at the bubbly distraction to the drudgeries of government. In no time, I'd spread my attentions from the House over to the Senate, where important senators were always popping out in response to my notes, just to pass a few lighthearted moments. After a while, people started telling me I was wasting my time being a little secretary and that, because of the pull I had developed in the corridors of power, I should have been a high-level lobbyist myself.

I also was assigned the glamorous task of ferrying VIP constituents to and from the airport in Bright's familiar gray limousine, complete with telephone. I'd call up Bright and announce importantly, "I'm en route here," or "Galactic activity is heavy there."

Once in a while, I'd chaperon one of Bright's girl friends, shipped in from his home district for an overnight visit. They always went back the next day. The Lord giveth, the Lord taketh away.

Often, when I escorted prominent luncheon guests over to the House restaurant, I would be asked to stay. My effervescent manner and decorative value made me an asset at the lunch table and a pleasant distraction from serious business. Being one of the handful of women among two or three hundred males was a great feeling, nearby such celebrities as Tip O'Neill, Peter Rodino, and Barry Goldwater, Jr.

You go to the House restaurant from the Congressional offices in the prestigious Rayburn Building by a shiny, clean little railroad shuttle, which runs under the Capitol. I frequently escorted Bright's guests to the restaurant, and it was amazing the celebrities I bumped into while waiting for the train. Charlton Heston and John Gavin among them.

There were special cars reserved for Capitol personnel of rank, visiting diplomats, or members of state; but almost invariably, if the other sections were already filled with nonranking staffers like me or tourist groups, somebody would bundle me in alongside the "first class" travelers. I hadn't even come to the end of probation period, yet here I was already a Hill favorite.

Exactly four weeks after I started working for Bright, I was called upon to bring two distinguished-looking gentlemen, whose faces I recognized from the papers and on TV, over to the House restaurant to meet my boss. Even these well-known men were charmed and amused at having such a glamorous, personable girl as their escort, and I basked in their attention.

One of them raised the suggestion that I stay for lunch, and the other quickly seconded it. In deference to a lady's presence, the table conversation revolved around lighthearted topics, and eventually Lobbyist Bright escalated the fun by commenting, "Elizabeth here is the top person in our figures department!"

The two men, whom I'll call Kevin and Alex, chuckled, and we ended up spending a very delightful couple of hours together.

Later that afternoon, Bright called me in to ask me what I'd thought of his guests. I told him I thought they were very nice, especially Kevin, who had that winning combination of good looks, fame, and personality. I had to admit I was very attracted to him.

Bright was always trying to fix me up with people who had connections. "What can so-and-so do for you?" was his chorus. "He's not respected in this town." Power, he asserted, was the coin of the Washington realm and, without it, you might as well file for bankruptcy.

Kevin, he reminded me, was a very important trial lawyer whose fame had spread outside of Washington due to the Senate hearings. He was exactly the type of person I should get to know. In fact, he was going to do me the favor of fixing me up with Kevin on a sunset cruise the following night. All I had to do was bring along something to eat and one of my good-looking girl friends as a blind date for him.

Although I had worked on Capitol Hill for less than a month, I had already captured the attention of *Roll Call,* the weekly Hill newspaper, and given them an interview as well as a picture of me in a sexy, low-cut sweater. That issue was due to hit the stands any minute, and I couldn't wait for the publicity I'd get because of it. Not only that, but two weeks previously I'd been asked to film the first half of a pilot for a television series. The day of the sunset cruise I was finishing the taping, and I'd spent hours bouncing around in a bikini with a pin taped to my finger, bursting balloons for the camera.

It wasn't until about three o'clock that I checked into the office to get final arrangements for the evening, and it was a very irate Bright who came on the line. "What the hell have you gone and done to me?" he stormed.

"What are you talking about, sir?" I was astonished. Given my exemplary attendance record, I couldn't believe he was hollering about my taking a day off, especially in view of the fact that I would not be on overtime that evening.

"That damn newspaper story," he ranted, "about the Blonde Bombshell of Capitol Hill, what the hell do you think the taxpayers are going to say about that?"

The *Roll Call* story, which I'd neglected to mention to him, had hit the stands, and caused an explosion that made our side of the Hill look like Mount Vesuvius on a bad day.

The office phones hadn't stopped ringing and all lines between Washington and Bright's district crackled with calls from the oil people and from indignant legislators. Bright was fit to be tied, and I was fit to be fired, and all that saved my head, I'm convinced, was the extracurricular activity slated for that night.

The events of the day, plus the prospect of being with such powerful men on an intimate basis, plus my nervousness about being a playgirl for the first time, made me a bundle of anxiety. By the time I arrived at the marina with my basket of Kentucky Fried Chicken, and my girl friend Kate, I was on the verge of turning around and leaving.

Luckily, Kevin was a man of great charm, who put me at my ease, and the chilled Cordon Rouge champagne Bright provided helped as well. "May we live as long as we want to, and want to as long as we live," my boss proclaimed insinuatingly.

He was in his usual high spirits as we cruised across the serene Potomac on that gentle summer night, toward Anchor Island, and tied up near the Lady Bird fountain. "Just look at that," I rhapsodized. "Where else in the world could you find such a magnificent view of the Pentagon, the Lady Bird fountain, and the Capitol?"

"Beats me," Bright said, "but if you come across it in Des Moines, Iowa, I'll eat my hat."

The champagne was going to our heads, but our host insisted we have still another glass. "The only time a woman ever says no," he grinned, "is when you ask her if she wants you to stop." Then he began trotting out his favorite jokes about his star employee. "Poor Elizabeth," he tut-tutted. "She had that little chest cold again. Just look at the way it's swollen up."

As we got higher, the jokes got bluer, and in no time, Bright suggested that little Elizabeth entertain the gang with a striptease. "This girl," he practically panted, "has got a fantastic body, and she'll be doing you a disservice if she doesn't show you all of it."

Well, time was flying, and there was no point in procrastination, so inhibitions were soon shed, along with most of my clothing, and I was bumping and grinding sinuously before the stony gaze of our former First Lady.

Everyone applauded merrily when I refused to remove my panties, then Bright took me aside and asked me to go on upstairs to the cabin with Kevin. "Wait a while, please," I urged. "I don't even know him."

"Come on, be a sport," he insisted. "You do your thing, and I'll do mine." So Bright went off with Kate, and I went upstairs with Kevin. The flybridge was decorated with a white fur throw, and a hi-fi played softly in the background, but when Kevin made some advances, I had to tell him, "Listen, I just can't do it. I don't know you well, and I don't feel right about it. But how about dinner one night next week, when we can spend more time together?"

Kevin was very amenable and very understanding. I felt better right away, and even sucked him off, partly because he had been gentlemanly and partly because I didn't want my boss to put my job in jeopardy. Tomorrow was the last day of my probationary period, and the *Roll Call* piece hadn't made me feel awfully secure. Kevin and I did get together a few times after that, grew to know each other, and had nice, relaxed sex, just as I'd wanted.

After the party, Bright told me to take the next day off, both as my reward for a job well done and also as a way of letting the *Roll Call* explosion fizzle. It was a week before people stopped calling up to speak to the Blonde Bombshell of Capitol Hill, and a week before I was reassigned to orgy duty. This time, it was a little party for four at my apartment, where I cooked tacos while Bright and his associate both got it on with my bisexual girl friend.

After having sex with my boss, she came on to me, but I wasn't willing, so she moved on to my partner, who had been so active in my bed that he had nothing left to give her. It wasn't the best sex I ever had in my life, but it was valuable, because it pleased Bright and made him realize what a good sport I could be.

Soon, sexual activity had become a routine part of the job which I accepted, because this was the nicest I'd ever had it, and I loved being up in the ivory tower of power.

Usually, professionally oriented personal activity was confined to after office hours. However, I soon discovered there were social functions held almost every day somewhere or other in the Hill, during working hours. My own interest in going to these affairs quickly evolved into scouting missions for my boss. Such an occasion may have been a reception for an artist whose work was on loan to a congressman or senator for use in his office, as was commonplace, or one of the eat-drink-and-mingle parties organized regularly by the Hill secretarial group. I'd leave work early to attend, flirt, and have a fabulous time, and if I saw a girl who would appeal to the boss, I'd take down her phone number. Once I even brought a girl back to our office, and we started a little orgy on the green Naugahyde sofa.

After a few months, I began to develop an ambivalence toward this high-level erotic adventuring. On one hand, I resented being a sex commodity and would sometimes act sulky and uncooperative, while at other times I would be plunged into depressions. On the other hand, my assignments were assignments, and, in addition, I loved being in demand. For a person of my origins, this socializing, clandestine though it may have been, represented opportunity and achievement. Not only was I the playmate of some of the country's most powerful men, but I often played a pivotal role in getting through some bills that are national monuments today. I recall one particular bill which, if the truth be known, should be called "the Ray Act." Bright ached to get it by the Senate, and the night before the now famous legislation came up, I was assigned to entertain the Senator upon whom the decisive vote depended.

As usual, one of my duties was to provide female company for the boat party, and this time, I chose a beautiful girl named Clemmie, who was a real swinger, and my friend Joanne, who is happily married, but a political groupie.

Joanne drove her own car to the marina, but when she pulled into a spot far away from my brown Corvette, Clemmie and I got scared. Joanne didn't get out and come over, and the whole marina was pitch-black. Thinking she was a private eye, or the CIA, we rolled up the windows and locked the car doors. We heard heavy footsteps approaching suddenly out of the blackness, and I flashed my headlights into the stranger's face to catch him off guard. I thought I recognized him as the Senator who was my date, but since I'd only seen his mug-shot from the Hill directory, I wasn't sure, and prepared to drive off.

Just then, a familiar gray limousine purred into sight and out sprang Bright, late, but cheerful as ever. He immediately made the introductions and put everyone into a lively mood.

There was a brief delay, however, when Joanne, realizing we weren't going to sip Cokes and listen to records, decided she didn't want to stay, and had to be escorted off the dock, but as soon as the remaining four of us boarded the boat, Bright suggested we get down to fundamentals. In fact, he took me aside and urged me to take the Senator Boulder upstairs immediately.

I told him I preferred to get acquainted first, and besides, the Senator was a very attractive, pleasant person who would probably enjoy some conversation, and a little finesse.

"Let's sit down here and relax awhile," I suggested.

"Go on upstairs with him,"—Bright was impatient—"and don't mess around."

Under other circumstances, I would really have liked to get to know Senator Boulder. He was such a good-looking, charming person that, after we made love up on the flybridge, Clemmie crept in and tried to have sex with him. I was happy to learn there was nothing left for her.

Senator Boulder was a wonderful, considerate lover, very anxious to give me what I wanted and very appreciative of what I did for him. My boss was aware that both of us girls were hot for him, and I think it dented his vanity, but this was business, and he continued to behave like the life of the party.

Eventually we all got dressed, left the boat, and headed toward the cars. The Senator walked to his own car and Clemmie to mine, while Bright escorted me over to his limousine, where the reason for the evening's episode suddenly became clear.

Reaching into the back seat, he picked up a thick roll of official documents and spread them out before us. "This," he said, "is what I am going to get passed in the Senate tomorrow."

Which is exactly what happened. The bill was voted into law, and Bright received a note of gratitude from Senator Boulder, saying he'd had a marvelous time.

As my boss dropped me off at my house that lovely evening, he gave a satisfied pat. "See you in church, kid," he said.

5
High Times and Misdemeanors

By 1972, when I had really started to swing, I believed that if I stayed around Capitol Hill long enough, every interesting person in the world would come walking by me. Even Muhammad Ali came to our sacred mountain.

I met him in the Senate dining room where he was lunching with a group of senators. "Hi, I'm Elizabeth," I said, "and I'm on the staff of Lobbyist Elan Bright."

"You are?" He gave me his "trying not to" smile and eyed me up, down and sideways, "And just what is it you do for Mr. Bright?"

Ali was only one among the star-studded list of personalities, entertainers, best-selling authors, politicians, and statesmen whom I met through my position on the Hill.

Famous comedian Bob Hope took me along in his small party to the Gaslight Club, and I was right in the spotlight by his side when he stood up to receive an ovation, much to the amazement of my former co-workers there. Marty Allen told me I was beautiful enough to be in movies, when I met him through restaurateur Duke Zeibert. Likewise, Tony Martin and Paul Anka. And singer Glen Campbell actually gave me the shirt off his back, a status symbol from the Burning Tree Golf Club, when I was at his private party after his Shady Grove, Maryland, appearance. Hugh O'Brien, a D.C. regular, was constantly calling for a date.

Congressman Podell introduced me to Norman Mailer at the Palm Restaurant, and Peter Maas discussed the art of writing with me over a drink.

My political VIP list is too extensive to recite here, but to give you a sample: Senator Joe Tydings of Maryland sent me postcards from his overseas trips signed "Your cousin," and I was the dancing partner of the usually stern-faced former White House press secretary, Ron Zeigler. I even managed to win a smile from feared Congressman Wayne Hays, although I'd just stolen his parking place. Then there was the night the White House photographer rushed from a nude picture session at my place to photograph the First Family at the White House. And the time a famous industrialist cut short his golf game with the President to dash off to me.

I was involved in one amusing little incident, which was picked up by the papers. It occurred while I was escorting two of Bright's clients to the afternoon session of the Watergate hearings. Clad in an attention-getting miniskirt and tight sweater, I must have taken the Senator's mind right off the hearing. When the elevator door opened at the floor below our destination, I heard someone call out, "Hi, Liz!"

It was Senator Hubert Humphrey, one of my favorite Hill celebrities, so I stepped off the elevator to meet him. Senator Ervin, who couldn't take his eyes off my derriere, exited right behind me, not realizing it was the wrong floor until the door had closed, making him late for his session.

Another Hill personality I ran into all the time was a former astronaut. I had so much going at the time that it took me a while to schedule his dinner invitation, and, even then, our relationship almost didn't get off the ground.

This good-looking bachelor with the bouncy charm took me to Clyde's, a smart, excellent Georgetown dining spot, but when we looked at the menu, my space-trekking date discovered he didn't have his credit cards, and that his cash on hand would barely cover the price of a couple of hamburgers.

On top of that, when we hopped into his car to head back to my place, he discovered that his economic little Audi was out of gas. He had to thrust the car back and forth until enough gasoline drops splashed up through the engine to get us across the Key Bridge to the gas station on the other side. I couldn't help remarking facetiously, "Next time you go to the moon, be sure you take your American Express with you," when he asked for seventy cents worth of gas. Luckily, when we finally got back to my place, things improved considerably. And he remains one of the many nice memories I've collected around the halls of Congress.

Among my favorite places on the Hill were the luxuriant gardens that spilled down the grassy slopes to the south, and the reflecting pool to the north. I spent many peaceful lunch hours in these two settings, walking around, reading inscriptions on statues and understanding, completely, why tourists came to my city in droves. In contemplative moments, I would even compose a poem in my little pink notebook, to express how I felt.

When I was feeling more social, the bustling House restaurant was one of my favorite places to hang out. It was a terrific place to meet and get to know people, and many of my most unforgettable affairs began in that very place.

None of this, however, restricted me, because Mr. Ernest, the beautiful black man who, until his recent retirement, presided over the establishment for thirty years, always found me a place. Whenever I went to the House restaurant for lunch, Ernest would chivalrously pluck a rose from a vase on one of the tables and present it to me with a wink. And he would look the other way when I helped myself to the Members Only telephone, looking for a congressman companion to share my lunch break with.

One of my regular Congressional lunch partners was a dashing young Senator whom I'll call Player. Handsome, athletic, and married, this southern lady's man had been swinging with a couple of my girl friends, and they both gave him high marks as a lover.

Senator Player quickly took me up on my suggestion to call me at my office, but getting together was a hassle, because he was afraid of running into his wife. It wasn't until two weeks after we'd met that the wife decided to take the kids out of town to visit her folks, giving us the opportunity to be alone. By this time, we'd built up so much anticipation, we were both ready for a very romantic encounter.

It happened to be cherry blossom time, and the mid-spring evening was very balmy when we left my office. He suggested we go to his house, because he had to be available when his wife telephoned later on. We would take my car, he told me, because he didn't want to be seen in his with a young blond passenger.

Player had a lovely house in Georgetown, with a garden in back and a side entrance hidden from the street. He nervously dropped me at the side door before driving around to park the car on the street.

Well, it wasn't the first time I'd been smuggled in and out of a Congressional homestead. Incidentals like being snuck through the side entrance sometimes bugged me, but I'd try to shrug them off as a necessary part of covert activity.

Inside, the house was elegantly decorated with period furniture, drapes, and good sculpture and art. When I studied the framed photos in the library, I felt slight pangs of jealousy at watching my host with his stylish wife at official receptions, with his family skiing at Vail, or lazing in Caribbean cabanas.

In moments like these, I sometimes fantasized a powerful man like Senator Player would one day become the lover-protector I never had. But other times, when I saw what living hells some of those political marriages were, the dream died.

Some of those wives, who hardly saw their husbands because of the demands of his job, or his social or sexual activities, crumbled under the pressure. I felt sorry for some of them, especially the woman who was so helplessly alcoholic that they were always being evicted, because she would continually set fire to their apartment. Or the wife of another Congressman, who had become so irrational that she disappeared for days and turned up in a dazed condition in her car on some stretch of road outside the city. When I thought of things like that, I realized I was better off playing second lady to celebrity politicians like Player.

That particular night, I was satisfied with my role, for the Senator was an elegant and ardent suitor. He prepared a very romantic little steak dinner with salad, accompanied by a nice French red wine. Candles flickered on the table, sultry music wafted from the stereo, and my suitor left the room only once, to take the telephone call from his wife.

After dinner, Senator Player conducted me to the luxurious bedroom. He lit the fire in the grate, then drew me down next to him on the white velvet chaise. "I've been wanting to do this to you for a long time," he whispered in my ear.

We embraced passionately, exploring each other's face and hair tenderly in the semidarkness. As he caressed my breast, gently avoiding the already hardened nipple, he murmured, "How good you are to hold, how warm, and how much you turn me on."

He unbuttoned my blouse and slipped his hand inside to find I was without a bra. "My God, that's beautiful," he said.

He took my hand in his, drew it tenderly to his groin and let my fingers play over his big stiff prick. "See what you've done to me?" he crooned in my ear, as he slid my blouse down off my shoulders. "I want to make love to you now." He picked me up and carried me to the bed. Without bothering to remove the pale satin spread, he undressed himself quickly to reveal a tan, muscular body, and an enormous, beautiful cock ready for pleasure. He kneeled across me and removed the rest of my clothes. "I want you. I'm going to have you now," he whispered over and over.

Cupping my left breast with one hand, he began sucking and biting the nipple right. I was already wet, but as if that weren't enough, he deftly began to run his tongue in and around my navel, then down my stomach toward my mound. He parted my vagina as though it were a delicate flower, and slowly, luxuriously, began to flick at my clitoris, then slid his penis into my mouth.

Abruptly, he pulled himself away from me, fighting off his climax. "I want to be inside you. I am going to fuck you."

Then he was above me, raising my legs so they encircled his waist, supporting my hips with his hands, penetrating me slowly, rhythmically. "You feel wonderful, you're so gorgeous, you're so warm, so moist, so tight. I can't fight it . . . I have to. . . ." He came with such force that I immediately climaxed myself.

After we made love, he asked me to stay with him, so we spent a beautiful night wrapped in each other's arms. The next morning, however, it was a different story. In the cold light of day, reality prevailed, and my gallant lover had to figure a way to sneak me off the premises without attracting the neighbors' attention.

After serious deliberation, he decided the only reasonable strategy was to bring my car around to the side door, rush me out, and stash me under the canvas top, which would be fastened securely down on my side like a half-opened can of sardines.

Meanwhile, he was to remain in the driver's seat, perky as a bean, while I suffocated for God only knows how long. When I pointed out he'd been a lot more considerate the night before, he promised he would liberate me as soon as he dropped off some clothing at a dry cleaner on Connecticut Avenue. I went along with the scheme, but not very happily.

I mean, it really bugged me that it was just swell to eat and sleep with me, but being seen in my company counted as a cardinal sin. I was spoiling for mischievousness, and I meant to teach him a lesson.

The dry cleaner was standing outside his store when we pulled up, and he and Player chatted about everything from the weather to the price of cleaning fluids. While they shot the breeze, I sweltered under the canvas, with my ass on the seat and the rest of me twisted pretzel-shape on the floor. And to add insult to injury, the car in which I was being held prisoner belonged to me.

Time passed. Not only was the friendly neighborhood dry cleaner still rapping happily away, but by now, other neighborhood people had spotted the Senator and come over to say hello.

After five minutes or more, I couldn't take another "Good morning, Senator, how's the wife, the family, the this the that . . . ?" So I quietly slipped my scarlet-tipped fingers out from under the lid until they came to rest on the top of the door. I assumed Player would pick up on my signal, but he just kept on talking, so I began to wave my hand to catch his attention.

The conversation continued, but I heard an embarrassed cough from the dry cleaner, who must have been facing the car. I heard him say, "Well, guess I'd better, uh, be letting you get on," then the motor started, and we drove off.

Halfway down Pennsylvania Avenue, Senator Player flipped back the top, and up I popped like a blonde from a cake, much to the amazement of the passers-by. To this day, Senator Player has no idea how I stopped, or more likely started, the friendly dry cleaner's tongue a-wagging.

My relationship with Player lasted off and on for almost a year. After all, as long as it remained a secret, he had nothing to lose. I tried to be entertaining and considerate and to adjust my schedule to his. I didn't make demands, material or otherwise, and I was always the soul of discretion.

As anyone I've been involved with can tell you, I don't spread gossip around the Hill, and never leak juicy tidbits to the *National Enquirer*. Now and again, I'd confide things to a girl friend or to Elan Bright, but that was it. My boss was a safe bet, I felt, because he himself was into fooling around all the way up to the top of his politically astute head.

About Player, he was scornful. "What can that hick do for you?" he asked. "He's a nobody around this town."

When I pointed out Player was no run-of-the-mill legislator, but a nationally known celebrity, he merely insisted that glamour, looks, and charm had nothing to do with power on the Hill. He may have been right, but this time, I didn't care.

Naturally, my dashing young Senator couldn't squire me around town, so we would rendezvous at my cozy little apartment overlooking National Airport. Since going to a restaurant was out of the question, he would often bring along a couple of frozen TV dinners, which was about as much as I could manage to cook without burning the house down.

As our dinners heated up in the oven, Player and I would sit on the balcony, watching the beautiful spectacle of the planes landing against the setting sun. It was a very groovy time. He used to tell me how much he liked me, both sexually and as a person, and insist that he intended to keep our romance going for a long, long time.

He would stroke my hair, then I would settle into his arms. Soon we'd be kissing and caressing, turning each other on so much that almost before we knew it, we'd be inside making love.

Since he always went home immediately after our session, the dinners often got scorched, and soon, I began to burn, too. I started to ask myself where messing around with a terminally married man was getting me? You're single, I lectured myself, and you need a man to take you places, someone who will be with you nights and weekends.

Player was never going to fill the bill, so I started seeing lots of new guys, and, in the process, had to break some dates with the passionate Senator. I had so much going that I would make three or four commitments for one evening and wait until around five o'clock to decide which ardent politician or wealthy businessman would be my escort.

I always tried to call the rejects to cancel, but sometimes I forgot, which meant a couple of guys would often turn up at the same time, but fortunately, my absentmindedness never got me into serious trouble. Never, that is, until the "Affair of the Half-Frozen Casserole."

After I'd been breaking dates with Player fairly often for a couple of months, the Senator began to get irritated, then stopped calling altogether. Finally, I couldn't help admitting to myself that losing him bothered me. He was, for one thing, a very passionate lover. Also, while he would never stick out his neck for me, he did me favors like making the useful introductions that helped me along.

I just didn't want it to end, so finally I conquered my pride and called him to apologize for my rudeness. I confessed that I resented the fact that he never spent the entire night with me, and he told me, "I'll fix it even if I have to knock down walls." If he had only known what an omen that was!

Next day, to make sure I was interested in seeing him again, he stopped by my desk at lunchtime to leave me a message on Congressional notepaper, "I came by to see if you were really serious about wanting to see me. If you want me, please call. Mr. P."

I was especially touched the following day when I called to set up a date, and he asked me to suggest a day for him to sneak away from his wife. We decided on the coming Wednesday.

Telling his wife he was going out of town on business

was quite a risk, and in order to be convincing, he had to drop out of sight in the middle of the afternoon. I told him to come by my office to pick up my keys, and then to go over to my apartment to wait for me until I finished work. He stopped by about four, took the keys, and, telling me to hurry home, he split.

Right after he left, something came up that was beyond my control. My boss informed me that Congressman Ken Gray of Illinois and a lawyer, who had wanted to get together with Bright and me, had set up a meeting at the Palm Restaurant for that evening.

Bright wouldn't hear of me not coming. On top of that, I remembered that a couple of weeks before, I'd made a third date for that night with a well-known Senator.

There was no way of getting in touch with the Senator or with Player, because I'd told him not to answer my phone. On the promise that I could leave after one drink, I showed up at the Palm for my seven o'clock appointment with Bright and his cronies.

Bright, never the most punctual man in the world, was delayed by a House vote and breezed into the restaurant about eight. I sipped my drink and tried to concentrate on the company, but I just couldn't. By eight-thirty, almost two hours after I'd told Player I'd be home, I managed to leave, jumped into my car, and headed very fast through downtown Washington.

As I was coming off K Street, around the rim of the Tidal Basin, a Volkswagen suddenly appeared out of nowhere, and we slammed into each other with a sickening crunch.

Locked together, we careened for twenty terrifying

feet, coming to a halt at the very edge of the water. When the police finally arrived, they took forever getting all the details. "Listen," I announced, "I haven't got time to mess around here filling your notebook for you. I have just left an important lawmaker, and I have another one waiting for me over at my house and he is going to be very mad."

"Oh, really?" the cop said. "Please give him our apologies."

I arrived home to find Player sitting on the sofa with his coat over his arm. He immediately began telling me off as if he was my husband. "Do you know what time it is?" he fumed. "I'll tell you, it's nine-thirty, that's what it is! So where the hell have you been?" He wouldn't believe the car wreck until I offered to take him downstairs to show him the damage.

Still, neither of us wanted to write off the evening, for our own separate reasons. There were other things I could have done on such a beautiful early-summer night, and I didn't intend to waste what was left of it. He, having gone to so much trouble to get away from his wife, had no place else to go.

So we put the half-defrosted Stouffer's casserole in the oven, and while it heated, we sat on the balcony, sipping wine and watching the planes. Soft breezes played around our faces, and we looked into each other's eyes. "You know, Elizabeth darling," Player sighed, "I care for you a great deal, and I miss you when you disappear on me."

"Let's not think about it," I cooed. "I'm here, and we're together." As we kissed, I actually thought I heard bells ringing, not the heavenly kind, but the ones that warn you hell's about to break loose. It took me only seconds to realize that what was ringing was the house phone. "My God, who can that be?" I slipped out of Player's embrace and ran to answer it.

Of course, my caller was the eager Senator I'd completely forgotten about, announcing he was downstairs with a little offering for our dinner, and that he'd be up in a second. "Give me five minutes," I panted. "I'm on a long-distance call."

Player paled. "What the hell is going on now?"

"You've got to leave." I threw his tie, coat, and shoes at him. "Someone you don't want to run into is coming up."

I ran madly around, spraying air freshener all over the apartment to get rid of the cooking smells, while Senator Player dashed for the door, dressing en route. "Take the service elevator," I warned him.

When he was halfway down the hall, I called him back. "Here, you forgot this." And I thrust the half-baked Stouffer's casserole at him.

As the service elevator closed, the passenger car next to it opened, and out stepped a grinning elder statesman, prepared for a leisurely night of stolen love.

6
Goldilocks and the Three Unbearables

Congressman Billie Bob Blank was as outgoing and affable as his old buddy, Lobbyist Bright. I could tell from our first meetings that he was interested in me, and I was pleased when he actually invited me to join his staff. Even my boss couldn't refuse the request of a Congressman from a major oil-producing state, so off I went to the hallowed halls of the Rayburn Building, ready to begin a serious job. The job was serious, all right, but not quite what I'd had in mind. It also involved meeting a lot of people, but not quite the people I'd dreamed about. For instance, there was the character whom I'll call the Pudgy Contractor.

The Pudgy Contractor, as I'll call him, was a multimillionaire and generous to a fault, because his gifts always had very long strings attached.

The Contractor's main areas of endeavor were highway construction in my boss's district and political credit-collecting in Washington. He had a physiognomy only a recipient could love, stood all of five feet tall, and weighed three hundred pounds if he weighed an ounce. He was a crony of Lobbyist Bright's, but he soon became my problem.

The Pudgy Contractor was one corner of an influence-peddling triangle which included a state representative and, of course, Blank. The arrangement, built on a little back-scratching here, a little influence-peddling there, resulted in the Pudgy Contractor's being awarded lucrative rights-of-way contracts back home. Later, the pyramid crumbled under the weight of official investigations into payoffs and contract manipulating, but at the time the road builder crossed my path, he was a macadam Robin Hood, showering his gratitude all over town.

A pretty girl in my office had told me that the Contractor frequently took her to dinner, but even so, she couldn't have been more relieved to see him transfer his interest to me, as I found out one late-fall evening.

It was at a very active time in my private life, and it so happened I had a date with a guy I really dug. "I don't want to come and meet your friend," I announced to my boss, when he suggested another boat outing.

"Why not?" he asked, surprised I wasn't springing at the chance.

"Because I have an important date tonight."

"Well, break it."

"I can't. It's a guy I'm really involved with, and I don't want to screw it up."

"Well, then, do them both." He was getting resourceful. "If you join us early, I'll have you back home by nine o'clock."

Seeing no way out of this dilemma, I decided to go along with my boss's compromise plan and agreed to show up, at least for a drink.

To say the Pudgy Contractor was not God's gift to women would be to make the understatement of the decade, but he did make a heroic effort to be charming. He even expressed interest in my job.

"Well," he stared at my chest, "I can see you have a great future ahead of you." He capped off this witticism by blowing a cloud of acrid cigar smoke in my face.

After a half hour of sipping a drink and talking about nothing much, he realized his sex appeal wasn't getting him anywhere and decided on a different approach. All of a sudden he dipped into his pocket and came up with a wad of notes which he pressed into my hand.

"What's this for?"

"It's a gift for you." He pushed the money at me. "Buy yourself something."

"I'm sorry," I said, "but I can't accept it."

"It is without obligation," he pressed, puffing on his fat cigar, "so take it, and talk no more about it."

Three hundred dollars was, and is, a lot of money, but I didn't want to be obligated to this man in any way. "I'll have to ask my boss," I said firmly, and immediately went to find Blank.

I found Blank up on the flybridge with his date and explained the situation, to which he devoted two seconds of consideration. "Why look a gift horse in the mouth?" he finally asked.

"Because I don't plan on giving him anything in return," I responded.

"That's his problem," he retorted.

So back I went to Pudgy. "Okay," I said, "I'm accepting your kind gift. Thank you very much." I stifled a little yawn and told him I was tired and had to run.

If the Pudgy Contractor was annoyed, he didn't show it, but told me how nice it was to meet me, and how much he looked forward to seeing me again next time he was in town.

"Let's do get together," I said hypocritically. Anything to get away. At that point, I would have promised to spend Halloween with him, because I had no plans ever to see him again.

Alas, I was soon to learn that road builders bearing gifts are not that easily put off. A couple of weeks after the first encounter, Blank called me into his office to tell me Pudgy was coming to town, and to keep open a night the following week.

"Not that horrible slob," I pouted. "I don't want anything to do with him."

Blank was very quick to remind me I had accepted money from him and owed him something in return. "But it was you who told me to take it," I insisted.

"Only on the condition you did him," he answered, and that was an order.

The next week I went to dinner with the Contractor at the Jockey Club, and throughout the meal, he sparkled with stories about how phenomenally rich he was and what a small fortune the marble-sized diamond rings, which bit into the flesh on his fingers, had cost.

After dinner, we rushed back to my place, where we

drank champagne and quickly moved to the bedroom. Beautifully decorated with a thick white shag rug, red velvet bedspread and drapes, luxurious white fur throw, and red satin sheets, the bedroom had always been a specially wonderful place to me, and I resented the Contractor's being there.

I put some music on the stereo and lit the scented candles, none of which enhanced the charms of my lover-to-be, who was even worse undressed. He had a belly like a hot-air balloon, legs like the Alaska pipeline and a truly obnoxious bedside manner.

I turned out all the lights, extinguished the candles, downed a glass of champagne real fast, and closed my eyes, and climbed on top of him. I bounced up and down on him for a couple of minutes and faked some sexy moans and groans to make him come fast, which, thank God, he did. Afterward, I went into the bathroom and threw up.

When I came out again, he was on the phone calling a buddy back home to tell him blow for blow what he had just done.

"He's gonna be jealous as hell," he chuckled.

"Hey, old buddy-boy," Pudgy snickered, when his friend answered. "Guess where I am, and guess what I'm doing?"

It must have been two o'clock in the morning back home, and his friend was probably asleep with his wife alongside.

"You ain't gonna believe this," the Contractor slapped his big thigh. "But I am in a bed that's got red satin sheets and there's this gorgeous blond doll with a figure that's gotta be seen . . . and guess what she's doing to me?" I was incredulous.

"Dunno . . ."

"She is"—he formed his syllable slowly—"putting champagne on my cock, and now she's sucking it off!" He tried to give credence to his little bit of fiction by reaching over for my head, but I backed away.

"Uh . . . ?"

"And, guess what else? She's dying to talk to you." He cupped his hand over the phone and thrust it to me. "Say something sexy to him, honey. Make him real excited. Tell him you've heard great things about him and can't wait to get together."

I shook my head. "Some other time."

"Come on, Goldilocks. Her name's Goldilocks," he continued. "Go on, talk. Say something sexy to my friend, Nicky the Turk."

"Hi," I said, "How are you?"

"I'm fine," he said, and hung up.

The Pudgy Contractor had such a high old time of it that he couldn't wait to get together again. Naturally, I looked forward to his next Washington visit like World War III.

The social calendar was very glittering that winter of 1972–73. One major event was Richard Nixon's inauguration to a second term, and another event, for me, was a big charity's annual $100-a-plate fund-raising dinner in the Shoreham Hotel ballroom. My boss was an active member of this hard-working, altruistic group of prominent Washingtonians, who aid underprivileged youths.

A bunch of attractive girls would act as hostesses for

the big event, and Blank asked me to be one of them. A lot of important people, many of whom I knew, were going to attend, and I dressed my very best for the occasion.

I wore a long, slinky white dress with one long sleeve, which was laced with gold cord, and a skirt slit all the way up to the waist. My hair was a crown of platinum curls, and everyone said how much I looked like Marilyn Monroe that night.

I was the sparkling centerpiece of the evening, with everyone urging me to sit at their table. Needless to say, my boss felt good that his staffer was in such popular demand and encouraged me to circulate.

Art Sampson, director of the General Services Administration, was there, and so was the Postmaster General, to whom I was dispatched with a message. "Mr. Postmaster," I said in my breathy Monroe voice, striking a curvy pose, "I'm sent special delivery to you from the Congress."

He and the others at the table started laughing and making funny cracks, and asked me to join them. I was having a fantastic time, until Congressman Blank called me over.

"Elizabeth"—he was turning a cloakroom disk over in his hand—"guess who's in Washington?"

"The President of the United States and Henry Kissinger, for a change."

"And guess who else?"

"Who?"

"My friend the Contractor."

"Why are you telling me?"

"Because he wants to see you."

"When?"

"Now."

"You're kidding!" I was stricken.

"I'm not." And he wasn't. "He's waiting for you at his hotel, the Quality Inn on Capitol Hill."

"Not tonight," I pleaded. "Please let me stay here. I'm having such a wonderful time."

"Oh, come on," he said. "There's nothing here for you. Cast the bread upon the water, Elizabeth."

"With that guy, all I get back is a soggy roll."

"You'll never know until you try it," he urged me.

"Let me stay just a few minutes more," I begged, "and then I'll go."

Fifteen minutes came and went, and I was still flirting and having fun, when Blank called me over again. "Elizabeth," he said, lowering his voice so as not to be overheard, "you go, and you go *now*."

I tried outright defiance. "I'm not going."

"Fine," he announced coldly. "Stay if you like, but don't bother coming to work tomorrow, or any other day."

"Congressman Blank," I choked, "are you serious?"

"You're damn right I am," he said, fury creeping into his voice.

It was only ten o'clock, just the beginning of a beautiful night, but I left and went home to change. I was sure not going to show off my nice clothes to somebody like Pudgy.

While I was at home, I decided to call the Contractor in hopes that he had changed his mind, or better still, fallen asleep. No such luck. He was at the bar, mad as a bear with a headache. "Where the hell are you?" he snarled.

"I had to go home to get some aspirin," I tried playing on his heartstrings, "because I don't feel at all well."

"That's too bad." His compassion was boundless. "But I suggest you get your ass over here right now."

It was almost midnight when I drove from Crystal City to Capitol Hill, which is deserted and scary at that time of night, and it was a contentious little fat man who greeted me at the bar. "About time," he snapped, leading me immediately up to his suite.

I could hear issuing from the bedroom what sounded like wood being sawed, but the Contractor's bitching quickly drowned out the noise. "I've been sitting here starving all night, waiting for you," he said, "and I'm very hungry."

"Well, call room service."

"It's closed, and it's all your fault."

"What do you expect me to do about it?"

"You could go out and get us some hamburgers," he said.

"I've eaten," I replied.

He changed the subject for a moment, hoping to get me upset. "It's too bad you weren't here earlier," he carped, "because I had five hundred dollars for you."

By now, I was really fed up. This was really my limit. "Look," I hissed, "I don't give a shit if you had five million. I don't want your money, and I don't want you. Moreover, I'm not going chasing all over Washington at midnight looking for hamburgers. So fuck you!"

What I didn't know was that Congressman Blank had mischievously implied to this ape that I had a crush on him, and I'd deflated his ego by letting the cat out of the bag. He was speechless for a moment, during which the sound of sawing wood returned.

"Plus," I carried on, "I was having a wonderful time until you showed up and ruined my night."

That made him very mad. "Well." There was a cruel edge to his voice. "If that's the way you feel, you don't have to stay. Who the hell needs you, anyway?"

"Good," I said, "I'm leaving." I made for the door, but the Pudgy Contractor decided he wasn't going to let the evening fall apart just like that.

He stopped in front of me. "Before you go," he softened slightly, "how would you like to do me a small favor?"

"Why should I?"

"So that I won't put the bad mouth on you to your boss."

"What do you want me to do?" I asked, defeated.

"I want you"—he drew me toward the sound of the sawing—"to come in here and give Nicky a kiss."

"Who's Nicky?"

"Nicky? You know Nicky," he said it as though this was my long-lost father. "You talked to him on the phone that night, and you told him you were dying to meet him. Meet Nicky the Turk."

In we go to the bedroom, and there's another member of the King Kong fan club, lying face down on the bed, passed out drunk, snoring like crazy, shnawk, s-s-s-s, shnawk, s-s-s-s.

The Pudgy Contractor rolled his friend over on his back to reveal a huge hirsute belly. "Hey, Nicky old buddy, wake up, look who's here."

The Turk couldn't have cared less. He wanted to sleep, but when Pudgy kept nudging him, he opened his bleary eyes, then closed them again. "Hey, Nicky, wake up," Pudgy kept on. "Goldilocks is here to see you."

It was no use, so the Pudgy Contractor asked me to "Give my buddy a little kiss," which I did, on the cheek. Still nothing, so I had to kiss him on the mouth. When he still didn't move, I asked Pudgy to leave the poor guy alone. "He wants to sleep," I told him, but the Contractor, not to be thwarted, had one more suggestion. "Suck his cock for him," he rasped.

"No," I said emphatically, "I won't suck his cock. I won't kiss him again. I'm doing nothing more except walking out." And I did.

Sure enough, next day when I arrived at work, I was confronted by an enraged Congressman Blank, pacing up and down in his office before the Pudgy Contractor, who was sitting on the green Naugahyde sofa like a frog on a lily pad, wearing a parsimonious smirk and letting the boss do the talking.

"Goddamn it!" Blank stormed. "What the hell happened last night? Why did you jerk everybody around like that? You made me look like an idiot, and you ruined my friend's only night in Washington. He could have gone out with other girls, but he was nice enough to choose you."

I didn't have a reply.

"I think the first thing you should do," the Congressman continued, "is to offer my friend an apology for your inexcusable behavior."

My behavior? I started to boil, and before I could stop myself, I lashed out.

"I'm tired of being pushed around, being dangled around all over the place, and screwing all your cronies. Nobody ever asks me what I feel or what I want to do. All they want is to have their cocks sucked. Well, to hell with the whole scene. Don't expect me to do your friends anymore, especially this fat pig!"

The Pudgy Contractor flinched, and the Congressman bristled. "Elizabeth," he said, "why don't you just go and get your things?"

"What do you mean?"

"I mean you're fired!"

"Fired! Because I won't do your friends . . . ?"

"I mean get the hell out of my office."

I recovered my composure suddenly, and tried to figure a way to save my job. With my eyes misting over, I pleaded. "Don't make me walk out in the middle of the day like this in front of all the others. Please. Let me leave quietly later on."

If I could hang on for another hour, calm down, and go back and apologize without choking, I might have a chance. I went outside, got a Coke, vanished into the washrooms for half an hour, then returned and called Blank on the intercom. "May I talk to you, please?"

"Come in." He was abrupt.

So I went in and they were still both there, waiting for me to begin. "I want to apologize . . ."

"Then go ahead," Blank urged me, but I couldn't.

"Tell my friend you're sorry," he said.

"I'm sorry for messing up your evening," I repeated.

"And you didn't mean to call him those nasty names."

"I didn't mean the bad names."

"You promise to treat him better next time."

"I promise," I fibbed. Somehow, there was going to be no next time. And there wasn't. When the scandal involving him broke, he never crossed my path again. But even though he was gone, there was a third unbearable ready to take his place.

Number three was a state representative from Blank's district, and the two of them had been close friends for many years. The Congressman had told me more than once how helpful this local politician had been in getting his bills passed, and, in return, Blank did him all kinds of favors.

On our first date, the rep, who was not as unappetizing as the Contractor, took me to the swanky Jockey Club, and after dinner, I made an excuse. "I have a jealous boyfriend," I said, and this and that. "How about next time?"

Next time, I tried to be nice to him, but I couldn't go through with it, and now neither the state rep nor my boss took it gracefully. "Dammit," he said, "I need this guy. Don't louse me up again."

Our third meeting took place a couple of weeks after the Nixon inaugural, on a wintry February day when the rep was in Washington to talk over an indictment he was afraid he would have to face. His wife and kids were with him, and, as part of my daytime job, I had to chauffeur them over to the Marriott. It had been prearranged that I would meet him for a secret dinner late that night, when his wife thought he was meeting Blank. To make sure everything worked smoothly this time, my boss made all our arrangements, which consisted of a meal at the Hot Shoppe near my apartment, and dessert in my bedroom later on.

Blank dropped him off at the Hot Shoppe, and after we finished our meal, the rep walked me to my lobby. "Well, are you going to invite me up?" he asked confidently.

I definitely did not want to screw myself out of a job, but I couldn't face screwing him, either. "No," I said, "I guess I'm not."

"Sonofabitch," he said under his breath. "This is the third time you've done this to me, and I'll make goddamn sure you never do it again."

And, as it turned out, the state representative was as good as his word.

7
The Anderson Tapes

My punishment for the crime was not the ax, since rolling heads tend to gather attention. Instead, I was to twist slowly in the wind.

"Why should I sit you out front where everybody can see you?" Congressman Blank said, in a pleasant but practical frame of mind as he banished me from his Garden of Eden. "If people don't notice you, they won't bug me to fix them up."

I was transferred, like an interoffice memo, to a recently formed Senate subcommittee of which a crony of Congressman Blank's was chairman, and which I'll call "Out-of-Sight."

The offices, which I called The Cage, were in a two-room suite in the Congressional Hotel, just off the Hill. They were empty, apart from a couple of desks and phones left behind from the previous tenant, who split in a hurry when his big deal went sour.

There was absolutely nothing to do in The Cage, and I spent the time listening to my radio, which I took in to work, and doing other personal things like making telephone calls and doing my nails. From time to time, one of my friends from Congress would stroll over to plug me in to the latest news.

It so happened that the chairman of the full committee was a northeastern Senator—Otis Battle. He was famous as the most vengeful man in Washington, as well as the most powerful, and everyone deferred to him. I remembered meeting him once with Lobbyist Bright.

"Meet Elizabeth," Bright had said pointedly. "She's head of our figures department. Not only that, looks like she's got her little old chest cold again. Just look at the way it's all swollen up."

Blank was, at that time, seeking to push through Congress an offshore oil bill, and dangling me in front of the tyrant was one way of winning a vote. Battle smiled appreciatively and that evening, around six-thirty, I was routed down to his office for a dinner date. My job was shaky at that time, so I didn't resist.

Battle, a virile, imposing widower in his early fifties, with a shock of white hair and a no-nonsense manner, took me to Duke Zeibert's restaurant, where I discovered why people feared him.

I felt as though he were saying, "I'm the ferocious Otis Battle, goddamn it, and you'd better fall on your knees for me. And while you're down there, kiss my ass."

We talked about how he had gone from waiting tables in college to hobnobbing with royalty and heads of state on his numerous overseas trips.

After dinner, Battle had suggested coming back to my place for a nightcap, but I discouraged him by saying I had a very jealous boyfriend with a key to my apartment and that I wouldn't want a person of his eminence to be caught out like that.

Next morning, Blank's boyish grin turned to chagrin when I told him nothing had happened. He was afraid his bill would be jeopardized, and all week long he bugged me to compensate for my lack of cooperation. "Please don't louse me up on this one," he insisted.

So a week or so later, I went over to Battle's apartment, which was in the Watergate building overlooking the courtyard, did a really quick job, and got my little round heels out of there, feeling too much like a Hill hooker. Before I left, however, Battle told me how much he wanted to see me again, but I reiterated that I had a jealous boyfriend, which was the truth at that time.

A year had elasped since that encounter, and I didn't run into him again until I was parking my car under the Congressional Hotel on my way up to The Cage. He was on his way back from lunch, and we exchanged greetings. Then he asked me if I would like to have dinner that night.

"I can't, I'm sorry," I said.

"Why not? You still got that jealous boyfriend?"

"Yes," I said, "that's it." I started walking to the elevator, and he asked me where I was heading.

"I'm on my way to the office," I said.

"Rayburn's the other way," he said in his usual stony manner. He was still sore because I'd turned him down a year ago.

"I'm not in Rayburn anymore," I said, figuring I had nothing to lose by being candid. "Congressman Blank transferred me to the Out-of-Sight subcommittee. Didn't you know?"

"You're what?" He hit the roof. "What the hell are you doing there? That's my subcommittee!"

Battle took off like Halley's comet, and it was one time I was glad I was in The Cage, because I wouldn't have wanted to be in Blank's position. I went on upstairs and, sure enough, it wasn't too long before the incensed Senator Battle pounded on the door. "Open this goddamn door," he thundered, "Open up!"

I unlocked my cell and was confronted by the full firepower of Battle's wrath. "I want you out of here now!" he screamed.

I dutifully collected my belongings and shuttled back to Blank's office, where everyone welcomed me like the flu.

Release from the isolation of The Cage was like getting paroled from solitary, but I became so upset and angry at being shunted around that I decided to dream up a way to get even and insure my position on the payroll at the same time. And when it came to me, it was perfect. I would expose all to Washington's crusading columnist, Jack Anderson.

Several months earlier, a girl named Daphne, who had also worked for Blank, had taken to Anderson the story of her dismissal through sexual intimidation.

Daphne was a beautiful girl, with an impressive record for competence and professional dedication. She was also married, but Blank had the hots for her, and made passes which she always turned down. One night at my place, he came on to her very heavy, and I saw her tell him emphatically that she was not interested.

Blank was so angered by her rejection that he eventually forced her out, and, to retaliate, she and her attorney went to the press. The papers wanted to get deeper into the story, but Daphne decided it would be too much strain to get heavily involved, so she let the whole thing die.

Now it was my turn to tell all, and since I no longer had anything to lose, I took the critical plunge. Using every disguise I could think of short of moustache and dark glasses, I sneaked along the hall outside Blank's office to the telephone booth, put a handkerchief over the mouthpiece and a pencil between my teeth, and dialed Anderson's number.

"What do you think?" I whispered conspiratorially when the columnist's office answered, "about a blonde secretary from Capitol Hill whose boss wants to get rid of her because she won't date his friends?"

"Who do you work for?" a male voice asked.

Peeking out of the phone booth to make sure no one was around, I hastily said, "Congressman Blank."

"Congressman Billie Bob Blank?" The voice became very interested. I knew the Anderson team had been hunting around for a lead on the controversial Congressman's questionable financial affairs. So far, they were getting only dead ends, but this could be the break they were praying for.

The reporter, Nick Packer, wanted to set up a meeting with me right away, somewhere off the Hill. I suggested the Statler Hilton on K and Sixteenth because Anderson's office was on K, but for reasons best known to him, Packer wanted to meet in the modern wing of the Smithsonian.

I agreed to the place and suggested we meet the day after next, then tiptoed back to my office full of vengeful glee.

I found Congressman Blank in one of his affable moods, and I must say, when he wanted to, he could be very engaging. When he wasn't obessed with scheming and fixing, he could be understanding, amusing, and generous, not the kind to be shafted by a disgruntled fellow finagler.

Of course, I started feeling ashamed of what I'd done, which now smacked of treachery. My boss and I had been through a lot together, and despite the callous events of the last couple of weeks, he had done a lot for me. As impulsively as I'd informed on him to Jack Anderson, I found myself confessing everything. He knew that they had been trying to nail him for a long time, and he was flabbergasted.

"Jesus H. Christ, Elizabeth! Why did you do such a stupid thing?" he demanded.

Now I was really in a jam. I didn't want Blank to hate me for zapping him, but I had to come up with a convicing alternative explanation, so I decided the villain of the piece would be the vindictive Senator Otis Battle who was, after all, the one who had kicked me out most recently.

"I did it because I was upset that Senator Battle threw me off his payroll," I said, knowing I was in over my head.

Blank fell silent, formulating a counterplot. "Leave this to me," he said. "I'm going to call Battle, warn him they might call and tell him it was a setup to trap those trouble-making snoops from the newspapers. Then we'll try to salvage a bad situation."

The following day, none other than reporter Packer breezed confidently into our office, but froze when he saw me, reinstated at my desk, looking bright-eyed and bushy-tailed.

He backed out of the office and seconds later called me from the same public phone on which I'd contacted him. "What are you doing there?" he asked, incredulous, "I thought you'd been bounced!"

"Well," I answered sweetly, "my boss and I had a long heart-to-heart talk, and we've agreed to let things be. I've got my job back, and I'd prefer to let the whole thing drop. Okay?"

Definitely not okay. Having been tantalized by this much-needed leak, he was understandably reluctant to see it evaporate before him. Indulging in a spot of rule-bending himself, he hinted that he might have to do the story about the blonde on the Hill, anyway.

I ran immediately back to see my boss, to tell him the latest development. Instead of being annoyed as he had been the previous day, however, he was smugly pleased. He had spoken to his lawyers in the meantime and had decided to set me up to snoop the snoops. Carrying a tape recorder, I was to keep my appointments with reporter Packer as though I still had a grievance to air. In the course of the interview, I would get the zealous reporter down saying things that he ought not.

"Leave me out of it, please," I pleaded. "I can't handle something like that."

"Elizabeth," the Congressman inquired, "do you remember who was clever enough to get us all into this?"

"It was me," I was admitted.

"Then who do you think should help get us out of it?"

"Me." Once again, I was trapped.

Out I went and bought a Sony TC 55 tape machine, with which I was absolutely unfamiliar. I also bought a woven red hippie-style bag to muffle any sounds the recorder might make. The bag was not really my style, so I then had to buy a weird-looking dress to make the bag seem in character. By the time I was ready, I looked like Carol Burnett doing a comedy sketch of dementia.

It was a gray day in September 1973 when I walked nervously through the scaffolded entrance of the Smithsonian to keep my appointment. As I entered the building, I switched on my recorder, which gave me forty-five minutes of tape, hopefully more than I needed.

I crossed the white marble floors to the secluded area near the cherub and swan statue which had been chosen as our rendezvous spot. I spotted Packer standing against the guard rail, and I walked over to meet him, knees trembling slightly. Here I was, a little secretary trying to get the goods on an experienced investigator. I felt I didn't have a chance. He led me over to the leather-covered benches alongside the fountain, and, luckily, the gentle playing of the water helped drown out any unexplainable noise from the recorder.

Ten precious minutes of tape had already expired by the time we got down to brass tacks. Reporter Packer opened by asking me what I knew about the Congressman's finances, his limousine, boat, and the helicopter he was reputed to own.

"I believe he does have these things," I said, blinking.

"Well, *I* know that," he said. "But have you seen any documents or records regarding them?"

"Gee, I wouldn't know where to start looking."

Packer told me that what they were after would most likely be on plain stationery, not official embossed stuff. Once I had located this potentially incriminating material, he told me, I should Xerox it.

"I can't do that," I said.

"Why not?"

"It would be dangerous."

"Well"—he was getting slighly impatient—"would you agree to unlock the door and let me come in at night to do it?"

"Oh, no!" My eyes widened with shock.

I was feeling sort of sorry for him because he was trying to perform what he believed to be a genuine public service, and here I was turning his head around. Changing the subject for a moment, I asked him about himself. "How did you get your job with Jack Anderson?" I inquired.

"Just walked in off the street one day."

"Off the street?"

"Yes," he said impatiently.

"What were you doing on the street?"

"Looking for a job."

"Didn't you have a college degree?"

"Yes," he said, "I went to college in New York. Now, can we get back onto the subject, please?"

"Sure." I was quite anxious to get my ass out of there, but there was one thing the Congressman had ordered me to get down, and I was leading up to it. It was 12:35 P.M., and the machine had been whirring since noon, which meant there were only ten minutes left before the tape ran out.

"Well, are you going to help us out?" Packer persisted.

"Only if it's not damaging to the Congressman," I announced righteously.

Packer said there was no way it wouldn't be damaging, and strongly hinted that, even if I didn't go along, he might expose the juicy scandal about the bosomy blonde on the Hill, anyway.

"You'd really do that?" I asked him.

"I sure would." He wasn't kidding.

"That would be blackmail, wouldn't it?" That's what I had been primed to say.

Unknown to Packer, Blank had also sent along a woman attorney as a witness to the meeting. She was disguised as a gallery buff, complete with pad and pencil, and she was pretending to sketch a sculpture collection. By now, I was sure the poor thing was getting tennis elbow. As for me, I had just gotten what I wanted, and it was time to run.

"Listen," I was afraid he'd notice the shakiness in my voice. "if I'm not back in my office by one, my boss will become suspicious and wonder where I am. I've got to run."

I jumped up to run out, but Packer insisted on walking me to my car. I didn't want to make him mad, because I was afraid that if I did, he'd write the story about me. If that happened, I'd definitely lose my job.

Pretending to look for my keys, I plunged my hand into my purse and turned off the tape recorder.

I drove straight back to the office where I called Congressman Blank, who was somewhere else in the building, and arranged to meet him in the meditation room of the Capitol. The meditation room is a dark, silent place where men are supposed to commune with their souls, but it's also the perfect setting for a secret conference.

Blank arrived, anxious to hear the evidence, which we listened to in the thin needleshaft of light. "That's blackmail," he repeated the words gleefully, then he thanked the Lord.

Next day, a newly cleansed Congressman Blank invited Jack Anderson himself up to his office to discuss the facts of the case, and somehow, everybody agreed to forget the whole episode. The Anderson caper had been a close call for a lot people, but my boss and I agreed that all's well that ends well, and off we gleefully went to our next evening's excursion.

8
Mistress U.S.A.

I entered beauty pageants in much the same spirit most people enter politics—with high ideals and ambitions. Similarly, I had to make some adjustments here and there along the way.

In a two-time swing along the contest campaign trail, I discovered, among other things, that as a front-runner I was required to be an adroit back bender, and that the chicken in every pot was usually me.

I was introduced to the glittering world of pulchritude-packaging in 1971, the year a former Miss Virginia, Gail Renshaw, won the title of Miss World and glided off the runway into the arms and fame of Hollywood personality Dean Martin. She was a country girl just like me, and her success convinced me that the way to becoming a real somebody was via the wholesome and prestigious pageant circuit.

I made inquiries into who handled entries in my area,

and found out the local star-maker was a man named Lew, whom I called. He told me to fill in an application form he would be sending me, and to bring it around. Dressed to kill in a tight red sweater and micro, I arrived at his door, entry form in hand. He was sufficiently impressed to invite me to dinner that night in order to discuss physical attributes and talent guidelines, and the way he told it made it sound very exciting.

He explained that the title of Miss Rosslyn, Virginia, was still available and saw no reason why I couldn't qualify. Then he assured me that I certainly had the necessary appearance and pleasant personality to become a contest winner.

The girl who became Miss Rosslyn, Virginia, would qualify for the Virginia State title, to be held only ten days later in Richmond, Virginia. In addition, the winner would get gift certificates, guest appearances, personal publicity, and become eligible to try for the national crown later in the year.

When I went home that night, I walked on air, certain I already had one slender foot on the star-spangled ladder to fame. Next afternoon, I called Lew to see where we stood. "Listen," he said, "how would you like to come over to my place for a cocktail? I think we can work something out."

Over a glass of champagne, he revealed that most of the applicants paid $100 for the privilege of entering the contest. However, knowing I couldn't afford the $100, he told me he would suggest other ways I could make up the entry fee.

I knew I would have to pay dearly, but there was no way I wanted to surrender the imaginary crown I'd been wearing for the past twenty-four hours. I definitely paid in my own special way, and won my first beauty queen title, Miss Rosslyn, Virginia.

Lew was no winner himself. A bearish man with a snaggletooth and a five o'clock shadow, he spoke with the elegance of a semiliterate and had a body odor that could drop a moose at forty paces. Despite all that, he dressed like a store mannequin in three-piece window-pane suits and two-tone shoes.

When he wanted me to put down another payment toward my success, I refused. He told me he had bought the judges and could rig the votes, and I was sure he could, but even certain victory wasn't worth another romp with that creep, which I told him as politely as I could. He was furious at my refusal, and he threatened to withdraw my entry. While I knew he could take other vengeful measures if he so chose, I also knew it was too late to cancel me, since my name was already in the program, and the pageant was only two days off.

With the slim pickings from my bank account, I bought a one-piece blue swimsuit and a beautiful, long-sleeved, turquoise evening dress, and had just enough money left to cover my round-trip ticket to Richmond.

When I arrived at the pageant site, I was heartened and surprised to see that, of the twenty other contestants, only five would be real competition.

Sashaying around in tight sweaters, hotpants, and boots, I was immediately singled out by the newspapers and radio for pictures and interviews, and my hopes climbed still higher after the Thursday rehearsal for Saturday's main event, when the emcee told me he thought I was by far the sexiest-looking girl there.

The emcee was an Ivy League type named Charles who looked as though he had been clipped from the pages of a Brooks Brothers catalog. Charles was accompanied by his wife, Lola, a former beauty queen, who agreed that I really stood out in the group, but I could use a little polish on my walk.

When this experienced and influential couple offered to coach me, I risked disqualification by sneaking out of my room and up to their suite after the nine o'clock pageant curfew.

They were relaxing in their robes, watching television in the bedroom when I arrived and, to my astonishment, openly smoking marijuana. I was broad-minded, but I never used drugs, nor did it seem to me that smoking grass fitted in with the pageant image. When they offered me a joint, I declined. "It will make you less uptight for the whole thing," Charles urged me, but I still abstained.

The effects of the pot made Lola sway slightly as she walked up and down the room, demonstrating the unmistakable beauty queen strut, brisk yet purposeful, feminine, and graceful.

"Now let's see you try," she coaxed. Lola, one of the most dazzlingly beautiful women I'd ever met, had a way of talking that evoked wicked assignations, both in the distant past, or the immediate future.

I walked around, trying to imitate her confident step. "Great, great," said Charles from the armchair. "You're getting the hang of it just fine."

"Try to hold your head back a little further, and relax your arms more near the wrists," Lola encouraged. "That's it. You've got the knack."

"Next, Lola suggested I work more on my posture, especially around the midriff, where I tended to slouch. I felt so fortunate, I just couldn't believe they would take so much trouble over me.

Lola placed one hand against the small of my back and the other firmly against my diaphragm. "Concentrate on this area here," she said in her provocative voice.

There was something about the way she touched me that was beginning to make me uncomfortable. Then, suddenly, before I realized what she was doing, Lola's hand had moved from my midriff and began caressing my breasts.

I recoiled. It's the marijuana, I thought, looking to her husband for assistance, but Charles's grass-glazed eyes were wide as saucers, taking it all in. "Elizabeth, honey"—he moistened his lips—"you've got a fantastic body, so why don't you let Lola love you a little?"

So this was what they had in mind all the time. I wanted to run, but I didn't move. They had promised to help me, and I didn't want to destroy my chances now. Besides, I rationalized, this couldn't be any worse than the investment I had already made with Lew.

When Lola led me to their bed and dropped her negligee to reveal a flawless, creamy body beneath, I did not protest while she made love to me as Charles sat in his chair, emceeing and masturbating.

It was very late when I finally crept back to my room after participating in their depravity, assured I had guaranteed myself a place in the annals of beauty history.

What the libidinous, perfidious emcee had neglected to mention was that the judging had already taken place at the Thursday rehearsal, that I had already lost, and that he had known it from the beginning.

I felt so disappointed and used when I was not among the finalists on the big night, that I threw all my things into a suitcase, ran for the first bus back to Washington, and cried the whole 250-mile overnight journey, vowing never to enter another beauty contest again.

It was in the fall of 1972, while I was working for Lobbyist Bright, that I heard dear old Lew was no longer associated with the contests. With Lew gone, I was sure I would have a better chance of becoming a beauty queen.

By now, I had more polish and self-confidence, and a better understanding of the circuit machinations and the way everything was supposed to fall together. While I was still as star-struck as ever, I'd play this one cool and straight.

I plucked up the nerve to call the head of the organization in New York, a Mr. Harvey Topps, who listened to my tale of woe and assured me my first unpleasant experience with Lew and his ilk would be no obstacle to my entering again.

As a preliminary, he asked me to send him a nude picture of myself, which I did; and, very soon after, he invited me to meet him in New York to talk over some details. Things were already looking brighter.

It was a gorgeous October day when Mr. Topps met

me at La Guardia's Eastern Airlines shuttle terminal, drove me straight to the airport Sheraton, less than five minutes away, and escorted me straight to the room he'd taken.

The room was a dismal sort of place, decorated in typical motel gothic: double bed, chair, bureau, and just enough floor space to swing a cat. As soon as we arrived, he phoned down for sandwiches and bloody marys, which I gratefully accepted, even though I don't drink, because I was very nervous being there.

While we ate, he showed me pictures of the big judging night, and you could almost touch the magic of the footlights, the cameras, and the audience. There were one or two pictures of Gail Renshaw, being crowned Miss World by Bob Hope.

Gee, this is exciting, I thought, and explained to Mr. Topps that I had dined with Mr. Hope in Washington and that he was one of my favorite people. He was definitely impressed by my connections.

After we finished lunch, he asked me to go into the bedroom and change into my swimsuit so he could see how I shaped up. I did, then paraded around to his approving glances.

"Walk like so," he said, indicating much the same gait Lola had shown me. "Carry the hand to the side. Let me see your fingernails, Hmmm, your hair is nice, your makeup is nice, your features are nice. The only thing that needs a little work is your smile."

He understood perfectly when I told him I was tense because of who and what he was.

That led to a discussion of my ambitions, goals, and feelings about the beauty pageants. Mr. Topps asked me if I had any special hobbies or talents, and how I thought I would adjust to becoming a star. He seemed to feel I really had a chance, and I was honored he was taking the trouble to explain everything to me.

When we got onto the subject of his personal life, he told me he had been ill, poor man, with cancer. "Oh, what a shame," I said. "What kind of cancer did you have?"

"It was cancer of the prostate gland," he said, then told me they had been forced to take off his penis.

"You poor thing," I sympathized. "You're not able to have sex." He was in his late sixties anyway, short and bald with a potbelly, and there was definitely no way you would turn around to look twice at him on the street. What a relief that here was at least one man who would not make demands upon my body.

"Oh, but the beautiful thing is," he beamed, "I can still have sex."

"How can you have sex if you don't have a penis?" Oh Jesus, no, I thought.

"Well, I'll show you," he said.

"Order me another bloody mary first, please," I said, going into the bathroom to apply the contraceptive cream I automatically carried around in my purse by now. I was too upset to realize I didn't need protection with a man who didn't have a penis.

He was already in bed when I returned. Turning off the lights to spare myself the sight, I climbed in beside him. "Here," he said, putting my hand on a certain spot I was supposed to gratify orally.

It was awful. He felt like a prune pit in my mouth, but luckily, ejaculated straight off.

Before I took the plane back to Washington, Mr. Topps, a man with more honor than his predecessor, Lew, promised me I would definitely be crowned Miss Virginia by Bob Hope. While he could not guarantee the national title, I would at least be among the twelve finalists at that level.

Time went by, and I was working for Congressman Blank but keeping in touch with Mr. Topps.

It was around April 1973 when he called to say everything was fixed for me to become Miss Virginia. All I needed was the $250 fee, which had to be provided by a business sponsor. I asked a well-to-do friend to send one of his company checks for which I would reimburse him.

It so happened that the organizers didn't have anyone to run the Virginia pageant that year, anyway, so they just sold off the state. When Mr. Topps received the check he called and said, "You're Miss Virginia. Congratulations."

I now had my second beauty title and was about to try, amid fierce competition, for national recognition as Miss U.S.A., which took place the week I was banished to Congressman Blank's Cage.

The big contest was held in New Orleans, where I arrived bearing the requisite courtesy gift, in my case a Congressional keyring for Louisiana Governor Ed Edwards. The other girls' gifts were from local Jaycees or chambers of commerce, but since I was the maverick, I said mine was from Congressman Blank, my boss. I felt an additional sense of belonging when the Governor graciously accepted the gift and told me they had been colleagues together at one time.

Most of the girls came with chaperons and relatives for moral support. In fact, one girl, who had not even been among the fifteen finalists the previous year and was determined to do better this time, brought her entire family along, including father, mother, and stepmother. The trio spent the week wining and dining the judges while their little girl remained closeted in her room being a goody-goody.

While I certainly didn't have a family to lobby for me, I had my own natural advantages, plus the chance that Mr. Topps would put in a word for me somewhere. But I rejected a judge's invitation to come by for a drink. I had already been in that kind of hot water and was not going to cook my goose again.

Emotions rose to fever pitch on pageant night. The big ceremony was being covered live by television, and we were very aware we were being watched by a huge audience. Somehow, despite tears, fears, and little tantrums here and there, we managed to get through the stage parade to wait for the result.

You could have heard a pin drop as the names were called: Texas, the Lone Star State; New Jersey, the Garden state; Arizona, the Home of the Grand Canyon; Colorado, the Centennial State; Pennsylvania, the Keystone State; New York, the Empire State; Illinois, the Land of Lincoln; and so on. There was even a winner from my home state, North Carolina, but no mention of Miss Virginia.

This time I was not depressed, just angry and disappointed. Dream Street, I decided, was nightmare alley as far as I was concerned, and the star-spangled runway was not littered with gold, but paved with broken promises.

Once again, I ran back to my room, packed my bags, cursed Mr. Topps and his crowd, and, not caring a damn who saw the tears rolling down my cheeks, prepared to get myself out of there.

On the way downstairs, I ran into one of the head judges, who offered words of comfort. I don't know what it is about me that people just don't give up on, but even after I'd lost, this man wanted me to come up to his room for a glass of champagne and an explanation of why I had *not* won, and who had *not* voted for me!

9
The Dirty Tricks Department

By Christmas, 1973, I decided that, one way or another, I knew enough socially desirable Washington people to launch myself a career as a party giver, and Perle Mesta, beware!

Bolstered by the success of an impromptu affair I'd given the previous year, I had Uncle Sam's printing presses produce one hundred formal invitations which I mailed out to a spectacular list of guests. Despite the fact that my party was to be on a weeknight, during the intense Washington social season, the response was spectacular.

Among my guests would be prominent lawyers, top doctors, television executives, industrialists, restaurateurs, entertainers, sportsmen, White House personnel, and at least one dozen congressmen.

As I proudly saw it, the only major difference between Mrs. Mesta's glittering affairs and my shindig was a technical one. While her soirees emphasized intellectual stimulation, mine would attract a more action-oriented group, for even though invitations were sent to Mr. and Mrs., most of the men arrived stag.

As soon as the invitations went out, word began circulating around the Hill that at Elizabeth Ray's parties, there were no women over 30 and no men under fifty. This was not strictly true, although I did plan to have an almost unlimited supply of gorgeous-looking girl friends who enjoyed partying. For this bash, I made sure there was a live band, lots of food and drink, and a crowd looking for a good time. The party turned out to be such a huge success that it went on all night, and dawn was spilling across the crisp yuletide sky when I finally persuaded the last guests to go home, leaving two attorneys, a Congressman, three Hill secretaries and me in a mischievous mood.

One of the secretaries, a senior girl named Roberta, retreated to the sofa, where she sat primly with her blind date, a lawyer, wondering why she had stayed behind and what was going on. She had been shocked when my partner, a lawyer with the looks and body of Robert Redford, threw off his clothes and started disrobing me.

The lone Congressman, who had desperately been trying to seduce the third girl, Cornelia, sprang at the chance to drag her onto the king-sized bed and start tugging off her clothes. He had already removed her earings, necklace, hair clips, shoes, and skirt when she decided not to let him go any further.

Four of us were rolling noisily around the bed, girls on the inside, men on the outside, when I noticed Roberta silhouetted against the doorway, aghast and on the verge of fleeing.

At that moment, the rest of us fell off the bed in a hilariously giggling heap on the floor, and Roberta shrugged, asked herself why she had always been so inhibited while the rest of the world was having such a gay old time, ran back to her happily astonished mate, and had passionate sex with him on the sofa.

The next day, people came by to claim jewelry, undershirts, suspenders, socks, ties, bras, and a coat or two. This boisterous finale capped what had been one of the most stunningly successful nights of my life, and I had to congratulate myself for having arrived, on my own terms, among the jet set. But, in the clear light of day I was compelled to wonder if what I had to offer the *in* people, which was definitely beauty and not brains, was of an enduring nature.

Looking back, I was justifiably proud of the distance I'd come from the hog days of my past. Still, I couldn't see real stardom illuminating my future. I vacillated between the excitement of having arrived and the depression of knowing deep down that the special life I led offered only condiments, not a whole satisfying meal. Eventually, I decided that if I were going to shoot for stardom, I should blast off right away, so I took a big step and got myself accepted at the N.Y. Academy of Dramatic Arts in New York.

Congressman Blank did not discourage me from resigning, effective December 31, and out of gratitude, I suspect, he and Uncle Sam kept me on the federal payroll until January 31.

Stowing my hi-fi, my car, and my furniture with a

friend, I moved to New York and launched into my new career. I became completely involved in my determination to become an actress, but getting to school was something else again. Each morning, I walked five blocks in the snow, hung onto a strap for twenty blocks, and walked another five with my hands frozen.

Living conditions weren't anything like I'd been used to, either. I stayed at the Barbizon, an all-women's hotel, in a room the size of a broom closet. The narrow single bed was hardly big enough to turn around in, there was a telephone without a dial, no television at all, and a bathroom I shared with the faceless occupant on the other side of a partition.

For three weeks, I searched for an apartment to share, but either I didn't like the other girls or they didn't care for me. Meantime, I returned every evening on a crowded bus to my crummy little hotel room, depressed by vivid memories of luxurious living.

By the beginning of my fourth week, I started thinking that there had to be a better way to become an actress than this, and a few days later, I impetuously tucked myself aboard a shuttle flight and returned to the bosom of Washington.

While I looked for a job and a place to live, I moved in with my friend Arlene, whose husband had just left her. She had a big town-house, which she occupied alone, but, despite the space, I wasn't anxious to stick around for too long.

Arlene and I had been intimate friends for a long while and had been through everything together, including orgies and kinky sex, the kinds of scenes I had vowed never be involved in again.

When I was hacking a swathe to acceptance, I had gotten involved with powerful people on crazy and perverted levels, and Arlene, who was more a lesbian than not, participated energetically. I participated in these escapades because it was what had to be done in certain situations, but I never did like it. This time around, I wanted to steer clear of that whole unattractive mess.

I soon found my own apartment, but finding the rent was another story. I worked for a while for a hotshot government lawyer, but when his after-hours demands began to take up all my free time, I split. Next, I did a stint with another lobbyist who looked after the interests of a powerful union, but I just wasn't getting the chance to circulate the way I wanted to. When I stormed out of that office, I had to face the fact that I was back to square one and penniless. Yet again, I had painted myself into a corner, so I called Congressman Blank. He was basically a very giving person, but he had no budget to hire me.

The chivalrous but philandering Senator Player had forgiven me for the thoughtless way I'd treated him, but the suggestions he was making weren't what I was looking for. So back I went to the corridors of Congress, wearing my tight sweater and pants, to wait outside the House and, if necessary, to buttonhole the entire U.S. Congress to lobby for a job. I dressed in my tightest, most alluring clothes and flirted with the guys as they came out. Everyone, including the security guards, parking attendants, and doormen, was pleased to see me back, and many of the congressmen had suggestions similar to Senator Player's, but by then I'd learned that you can't live on love alone.

Eventually, the senior staff member of a subcommittee under the mighty umbrella of my peppery, powerful nemesis, Otis Battle, said he'd see what he could do.

The staff member invited me for drinks, which I warily accepted, as times were lean and getting leaner. He asked me to check back with him the following week, by which time, however, the rosy afterglow of my obligatory sexual contribution had worn off, and there was nothing but excuses.

First, the chairman of the subcommittee was out of town, then they couldn't dislodge the girl whose job I was after, and on and on. Eventually, under a persistent barrage of telephone calls, he admitted that his boss was willing to hire me, but that my application was being blocked by someone big upstairs.

I knew enough about the committee structure by now to be sure there was only one person in a position to do that, but I couldn't understand why he would consider me a big enough fish to worry about. Sure enough, the staff member confirmed that the stumbling block was none other than my archadversary, the fearsome New England curmudgion, Otis Battle.

Power is self-perpetuating and pervasive, that much I understood, and I decided if I was being barred from the whole Hill because of one minor infringement, I would have to meet politics with politics.

I called up Congressman Blank for guidance, and he advised me to approach the big man with candor and courage. I was to tell him I realized we'd had our differences, then ask him if there was any reason we couldn't kiss and make up.

I planted myself outside the door of the U.S. Senate, and waited for Battle to come off the floor. "Hi," I greeted him cheerfully when he walked out. "How are you?"

He gave me an imperious look, and nodded.

"You're looking very sharp," I said, running my eyes appreciatively over him. He was a good dresser and a masculine and attractive man.

He stared back at me, at my classic cream flannel slacks, and at my outrageously snug lime-green sweater. "You're looking pretty sharp yourself," he conceded gruffly.

Senator Battle indicated a corner out of the line of traffic, and I fell in step, launching into my prerehearsed appeal.

"Look," I lowered my eyes coyly, "I know we have had our differences in the past. But why can't we kiss and make up?"

This feared and eminent man regarded me for a moment. "What are you doing tonight?" he asked.

"Nothing," I murmured.

"Let's go to dinner." It was a command, not an invitation.

At dinner, I didn't ask him for a job because our relationship was still frayed at the edges, but I did ask him for a reference. "If you don't want to help me," I said, "I understand, but please don't hurt me."

He denied any knowledge of my blocked job application. "I didn't know anyone was trying to hire you. This is the first I've heard of it. I won't stop you."

After dinner, he wanted to be alone with me, and I thought, well, I need his vote, so I took him back to my place, and we made love on the sofa. I gave a command performance, and he was grateful, and said he would call me next week after checking with a couple of committee chairmen.

It seems it never rains but it pours, and things all started falling into place. The day after my dinner appointment, I landed a job in the office of a Republican Congressman from Arkansas, which was more work and less pay than I was used to. I was going to get $9,000 plus benefits, to answer phones and type, which I couldn't do and hated, but it was a Hill job.

Over the weekend, I was able to move into my new apartment, a spacious one-bedroom with a terrace, confident about paying the rent.

On Monday, I arrived at my new job uneasy because I knew they were going to expect me to earn my salary. At lunchtime, I checked my service, and to my surprise, there was an urgent call from Battle's office.

He had been looking for me, and when Otis Battle wants something, the whole Hill jumps. I called his office immediately and was put right through to him. He wanted to know where I was. "Out," I lied. I just couldn't tell him I was already in another job.

"Well, come by around six o'clock," he said. "I think I have something for you."

We went to dinner at Stouffer's, and he told me how much he'd enjoyed our night together, although he didn't quite phrase it as delicately as that. Then he said he had a job for me. Feeling I'd now acquired leverage,

I was forward enough to state my terms. "Well, you know I am looking for twelve thousand dollars."

"I'll start you at eleven thousand," he said. "You show me you can turn up at the office regularly and keep your mouth shut, and I'll raise you."

He hurried me through dinner, leaving no time to linger over coffee. Back at my apartment, I asked if he wanted a drink. No, he wanted me. He was always in a hurry, and the digital clock I kept beside my bed was to become one of our more indispensable gadgets.

I have to say he was a resourceful, imaginative, and very potent lover, and even though I was more than twenty years his junior, I often tired before he did.

We took a long shower together. He soaped my body with bubbles all over, then I sucked his cock, but not long enough to make him come, just enough to make him really hot. When that was done, we jumped into bed, and he screwed me fast and hard.

We hadn't talked much, partly I guess because his mind was always on bigger things.

"Listen," I said after a long silence, "I'm really looking forward to starting my new job tomorrow."

"Good," he answered brusquely, without giving me a glance. "Just make sure you keep your mouth shut, do as you're told, and don't go getting any bad diseases." And with those words was born the most flamboyant hate/love affair in the scandalous annals of our nation's capital.

10
A Day's Work for a Day's Play

I arrived early and eager for my first day's work in the super-plush offices of Senator Otis Battle, to the unmistakable drift of deja vu.

As in Lobbyist Bright's and Congressman Blank's office, the girls all looked at me, then at each other, and wondered why I was there. This was a question all of us (including the boss, whose disposition often depended on the climate of our tempestuous relationship) would ask over the year I was there.

"Are you here for a shorthand job?" one naïve girl seriously wanted to know.

"No," I replied hesitantly, "I, ah, don't take shorthand."

"Then what you here for?" she persisted.

"Office duties," I answered lamely.

Alice, the official manager, who should receive a Congressional award for forbearance, stepped tactfully up, fixed me a temporary desk in the corner, and handed me a letter to type.

"Oh, excuse me, Alice," I called her back from her own work, "but I'm not familiar with this kind of typewriter. Which is the on-off button?"

Patiently, she pointed to a prominent black switch, and I began to pound away at the keyboard like a mad concert pianist, anxious to prove myself. But the words were running off the page, and, in one paragraph alone, I made a grand total of forty mistakes. By the end of the day, I had made fifty separate attempts to get the letter done, and, three weeks later, with three hundred sheets of paper wasted and no end in sight, I told Alice, "I don't know what's wrong with me, but I'm having a slight problem with this letter."

"Don't worry," she said graciously. "Just get yourself a typing book and practice a little every day. You'll improve." Then she quietly handed the letter to someone else to type.

Although the emotional environment was a little scary, the physical one was strictly deluxe. Our view of the glorious Capitol grounds was unsurpassed, and our offices were lavishly decorated with crystal chandeliers, thick carpets, fireplaces, plants, and artworks, all in the Senator's excellent traditional taste.

As one of the pampered elite, I enjoyed privileges staff members did not, especially when it became known whom I worked for. With the Senator's formidable reputation, and my blond, sexy looks, doors that were firmly shut in the faces of others were flung open to me.

Whenever I drove into the parking lot on the Hill, dodging the demonstrators who waved banners about this and that, the duty policeman would wave me into the best parking spots. "Hi, Elizabeth, how are you today?" he would greet me, and I felt like a queen.

On more than one occasion I was awarded precious space over more senior parkers, and one time I was given the last remaining spot at the expense of Congressman Hays from Ohio, who had to go fend for himself on the street.

After my first diligent week of appearing early and remaining late, I slipped into my own private schedule, which included showing up at midmorning, going downstairs for a forty-five-minute coffee break, and circulating, on my way back, through the House and Senate buildings to talk with friends.

Once in the office, I'd slip a piece of blank paper into the typewriter, where it would stay until the end of the day. I'd make my personal calls, then go to lunch and come back two hours later, if at all. If I did come back, I'd go straight into Battle's office, and walk out with a grin on my face, confirming I was not hired for my shorthand, and then I'd leave for the day.

Frequently, my daily check-out with my boss took priority over urgent governmental matters, and one day I walked out after a lengthy discussion of my anatomy, to discover none other than Senator Edward Kennedy, cooling his heels in the anteroom.

I never felt I was depriving America's taxpayers of anything at all, but I did feel guilty because of the few girls in our office who actually did some work. We had about twenty people, mostly attractive women, on our payroll, but most of them were actively engaged in sitting around reading the paper. Naturally, I was the most visible of the less-than-dedicated women.

Once, in a fit of pique, a dedicated staffer followed me to the lady's room, where I was combing my hair for the hundredth time that day, and blasted off at me for being along for the ride. "I'm sorry you feel that way," I retaliated, "but there is nothing for me to do."

When we took the disagreement to Alice, the girl admitted she was really angry about a Congressman's wife, who was on the payroll, just taking up desk space, and about the boss's distant relative with the private office, from which nothing ever went on. Even if I was nonproductive, the angry girl conceded, I was at least entertaining. Generally, though, nobody dared say anything to me because they knew I was sleeping with the boss.

My relationship with Senator Battle was a complete switch-around from the ones with Bright and Blank. They had both kept me around to be pushed into scenes with every Tom, Dick, and Pudgy Contractor they met, and they made sure people who could be useful to them knew I was available.

But when I told my new boss about the nature of my previous job, he assured me everything had changed. Battle was very possessive and wanted me exclusively to himself, but whether or not he had the right to make that demand remained a constant source of friction between us. Our affair was the story of two strong people with mutually desirable commodities, exploiting each other while convincing themselves that each was getting the upper hand.

Unlike Anthony and Cleopatra, Battle and I carried

on without a twinge of worry about losing kingdoms and the like. I buzzed around demanding to be fitted into his schedule, while he grumbled and gave me a hard time. Any demand of mine provoked a command of his, to the point where I was expected to break any date, no matter how important it was to me. It could be a romantic evening with an old flame or dinner with a girl friend, that didn't matter because nothing mattered but Battle.

If I dug in my heels and protested, he'd threaten to boot me off the payroll. In one short period, poor Alice had processed me out a total of five times, but each time he'd call me back and ask, "Well, have you changed your mind? Are you going to see me?" I'd relent, and reenter the uncivil service.

As our affair got hotter, the rest of my life began cooling off radically. While Battle attended some ritzy do at a foreign embassy, or a reception for Kissinger or something just as exciting, I'd have to go home, or stay home and wait. He'd drop by late and keep his limousine outside while, an eye always fixed on my digital clock, we'd have what I used to call Wild West Shows. These performances were marathons based strictly on endurance, not enthusiasm.

Sex was by demand, and I was never allowed the time to get in the mood for it. We'd begin our evening with a rushed dinner at six-thirty, with no time for coffee or conversation, then to bed for two hours if the boss was tired and four if he was not.

Senator Battle had an amazing appetite, an incredible capacity, and an insatiable need to satisfy a voluptuous blonde more than twenty years his junior. His favorite bed game was seeing how many climaxes he could give me, and with each Wild West Show, I was supposed to add another, until I was faking a dozen or more. I'd try to trick him, but he'd always remember the previous session's record. On my twenty-seventh birthday, Battle decided I should climax once for every year of my young life, and if I could have gotten away with it, I would have told him I had just turned five.

At first, our trysts averaged once a week, since he spent Friday, Saturday, and Sunday in his home district, but after a while, he started threatening me that he might come back early or leave late as a reminder that I was expected to keep my weekend free for him.

One weekend, he really did call me from home to tell me to meet him on Sunday in Washington, where he'd be stopping over before a trip to Europe. That Sunday afternoon, we spent an energetic few hours, and the next morning, I was astonished to receive a telephone call from him.

In a weakened voice, he told me he was not halfway to Europe, but flat on his back at Bethesda Naval Hospital. He'd been taken there when he passed out with exhaustion at the foot of the steps to the plane.

After a while, I started asking myself, If I'm going to put in all this homework, four hours of screwing here and six hours there, why should I bother going to work five days a week? Accordingly, I adjusted my schedule to about two days a week, and when the boss was out of town, didn't bother going in at all. In one sixty-day period, my employment record showed an absence of forty-three days.

When people grumbled, my boss would call up and

scream, "Dammit, everyone's noticing you're not around, and they're all bitching about it. If you don't start coming in regularly, you needn't bother coming in at all!"

I'd continue to be bad, get taken off the payroll, realize my mistake, then call him up to say I was sorry and wanted to make up. At dinner I'd say, "Please, can I come back to work?" Then I'd be super-super nice, placating him with exotic variations on the ancient theme of love. With my reprieve assured, I'd buzz into the office for the next couple of days, pretend I was working, then vanish again.

Finally, I went so far that I was forced to resort to extreme measures to save my neck. During one crisis, I remembered he'd told me about a threesome he'd done in Scandinavia and would like to try again. Although I hadn't been involved in scenes like that for two years and wanted to leave them safely in the past, it was all I had left to offer.

"Fine," he said contentiously. "Get your girl friend Arlene." He'd heard about her from me and possibly from other sources, because her taste for orgies was quite famous around Washington. However, our relationship had been strained recently, and I didn't think she'd come.

"If there's something in it for her, she will," he assured me.

I called Arlene and leveled with her. "Listen," I told her "I have done many favors for you in the past, and you've got to bail me out of this one." I also passed on the word that Battle was willing to give her $100, and that my job hung in the balance this time.

Arlene agreed to join us, and we all went to Stouffer's for a hasty dinner, then back to my apartment, where things didn't work out according to the fantasy. She and I kissed and caressed, while my boss orchestrated the whole thing like the Great Dictator. "You kiss her left boob! Now, you suck her right boob!" and all that. Arlene was prepared to become more explicit, but I balked. "Listen," I said to the Senator, "why don't you have sex with her? I don't mind."

He did, and afterward drove her home, later, she but an hour was on the telephone to me, crying and calling him the cruellest man she ever met.

Meanwhile, Battle rang me on my second line and complained about the way things had gone. "What happened between you two?" I asked. "Arlene is very upset. She says you called her a whore."

"Well, she accepted my money, didn't she?"

"At your suggestion."

"Well," he snapped cantankerously, "she didn't do enough for it."

He was mad at me all over again, and, to keep both my job and my promise, I started coming in at eight-thirty every morning. I did this for four days in a row, until, on the fifth day, the most unfortunate thing happened: A woman driver slammed into my car from behind on the parkway, and I ended up in the hospital. I sustained two broken ribs, dorsal lumbar strain, and whiplash, and had to undergo prolonged ultrasound and heat treatment and therapeutic massage.

Understandably, I guess, Senator Battle found this excuse harder to swallow than my other farfetched reasons for not coming to work, and demanded to have sex with me. I told him that was impossible because of my condition. Fine, he said, then he would have them to suspend me permanently from the payroll.

To convince him I wasn't faking, I agreed to see the Capitol doctor, but even after the physician had validated my injuries, Battle insisted I go to bed with him. I protested that my injuries were too painful, but he said that unless I got it on with him, our relationship was over. I'd alienated him often enough in the past few months for him to make good his promise, so I agreed to go along with the threesome he was suggesting.

To my surprise, he had found another playmate to have dinner and excercises with us that night. She was a Chinese girl who worked as a Hill secretary, and I knew her well enough to be sure she wasn't a swinger. She wasn't enthusiastic about getting involved, but she was now part of a commodity trade, and it was a role she couldn't refuse.

While he encouraged her to drink a little more over dinner at Stouffer's, Battle asked the young woman about her future plans. She told him she wanted to go to college, and he promised to talk to her boss about giving her an immediate $1,000 raise to help her on her way. Rebecca of Sunnybrook Farm wouldn't have been able to turn down that offer, and neither did my friend. They say that Otis Battle is the power he is because he knows everyone has a price and is a genius at discovering it. That night, he struck gold.

11
So Long to You, Joe DiMaggio

Through all my years of waltzing around Washington, I have met only one man who could truly be called democratic, Duke Zeibert. To the Duke, all men are born equal as long as they equally enjoy the hospitality of his restaurant on L Street, which happens to be the scene of some of my greatest triumphs and calamities.

Duke, a big man in stature and in heart, is the kind who, when he asks how your day is going, genuinely wants to know. He is generous, gregarious, and nonconformist, with longish hair and a lived-in face, and he has moved among people of position for so long I believe he cares about class only when it's conspicuously absent.

On any day, his large, clubby restaurant is sprinkled with notable locals, as well as famous out-of-towners, to whom no trip to Washington is complete without a visit to the Duke's. Despite the popularity of his establishment, however, he never imposes snobbery in seating, and treats a stuffed-shirt politician with no more cordiality than that with which he greets his special friend, Betty Lou Ray.

Needless to say, I have always been a frequent visitor at Zeibert's, and Duke and his close friends always chuckle over my wide-eyed awe when I pick out a new famous face from the crowd. Among the people met at Duke's are actors Hugh O'Brien and Forrest Tucker, singer Tony Martin, Teamsters boss Frank Fitzsimmons, former Senator Eugene McCarthy of Minnesota, and chairman of the National Democratic Committee, Robert Straus, to name but a few. During the Watergate trials, I shook hands with Bill Hundley, brilliant attorney for John Mitchell; Judge John Sirica, that remarkable and gracious man; and many of the other involved personalities.

Taking my almost terminal case of celebrity worship one courageous step further, I always entertained secret hopes that one of these important types would help advance me toward my ultimate destiny as an actress. To that end, I ambushed an attractive man innocently attacking his London broil, when I learned he was Jack Valenti, the distinguished head of the Motion Picture Association. Jack couldn't have been more gracious, and greeted with amazing equanimity my unsolicited revelation that someday soon I planned to go to Hollywood to pursue my acting career.

Perhaps my greatest social triumph at Duke's took place the night of the Redskin-Cowboy football game. Our team had won and Duke, who had taken me to the game, decided to celebrate the thrilling victory by closing the restaurant to outsiders and giving an omelet and champagne party for some five hundred sports, entertainment, political, and industrial VIPs.

Basking in the honor of being the hostess of this jubilant occasion, I proudly took a seat between Duke's daughter Terry and former Senator Eugene McCarthy. In the course of the evening, Duke led me around presenting me to everyone. "Meet my fiancée, Elizabeth," he would kid me affectionately. "I don't know whether to marry her or to send her to camp."

Duke took me to all the big football games, even the out-of-town games, along with his ex-wife and her present husband. When the games were being played at home, we were always invited to the office of the Redskins owner, prominent attorney Ed Williams, for postgame celebration.

In that inner sanctum, I mingled with people like Senator Edmund Muskie, Senator Edward Kennedy, Mrs. Ethel Kennedy, and Henry and Nancy Kissinger. I don't know whether or not these people saw me as just a working girl, but they accepted me because I was the date of a man whom they had all respected for years.

During this happy period of my life. I became Washington's number one sports fan, and even had a blazing cross-country romance with a married television sportscaster named Jon, whom I first met at the Duke's. The affair, which was very much off-camera, consisted of my being shipped by air from astrodome to arena to stadium throughout the season and lying low in the hotel room until the game was over.

As I sat by myself watching the game on TV, it was a thrill to realize that the man upon whom millions of eyes were presently riveted would share my bed that night.

Eventually, I became an expert at wangling the best seats at the most important games. Once I actually commandeered Senator Battle's own seats at the Dolphin-Viking Super Bowl game in Houston in 1973. All I had to do was call one of the owners direct, and, using my position as Battle's secretary, get them to release the tickets to me. As I sat in my new blue satin jumpsuit, long blond hair blowing in the crisp breeze, protected by the enclosure above the 50-yard line, I was smuggly scanning the masses of have-nots when I noticed the Senator, shivering in Spookesville. He did not return my cheery wave.

Seated around me were prominent sports fans, and I kept saying to myself, Can you believe this? At one point, I even leveled my Instamatic at television personality Ed McMahon, and, because he was so gracious about it, I sprang at the opportunity to strike up a spirited discussion about a mutual acquaintance both of us hardly knew.

After the game was over, the real ball began, and fans, press, camp followers who always mysteriously appeared in groups, victor and vanquished alike, gathered in The Pit cocktail terrace at the Hyatt Regency to drink champagne. I was pleased to discover there were, as usual, a lot of people I knew, and one of them mentioned that the really select party was being given upstairs by a famous show business celebrity.

I'd only met the man once before, at Duke's, but I picked up the house phone to wangle an invitation from him for myself and for Jon, who knew this legendary figure by reputation only. Of course, we were instantly ushered upstairs, and I even got to meet and talk with the famous man himself.

Through Duke, I had met many wealthy sportsmen, one of whom was a wealthy Minneapolis industrialist named Carlyle, whom I'd seen many times, but never consented to date. However, when he invited me to Minneapolis the weekend of the Viking-Eagle game, I decided to accept.

The middle-aged, conservative Carlyle installed me in the best hotel suite in Minneapolis before bidding me a wrenching farewell to go spend the night with his wife. "Do you really have to run off and leave me like this?" I wept through my crocodile tears.

"I'm sorry, darling," he apologized, "but I'll make it up to you tomorrow." And he left, promising to be back before breakfast.

Satisfied Carlyle was safely out of my life until our eighteen-hour appointment next day, I dried my tears and picked up the phone to call Jon, who was covering the game for network. He was amused that I'd turned up again and asked me to come over to the Marriott to spend the night.

Next morning, I snuck back to my hotel bright and early to find that Carlyle was already there. He had a face as long as a football field, and angrily demanded to know where I'd been.

Unfortunately, he had been so conscience-stricken by the thought of my voluptuous young body pining alone, that he'd invented an emergency in Washington and told his wife he was leaving town immediately.

He had then doubled back to our hotel and spent the

rest of the night staring at the curlicued ceiling, wondering where in the hell I was.

Despite his temper, Carlyle didn't want to hold a grudge, and immediately began urging me to make love.

Having spent the night with the much younger and virile Jon, all I wanted to do was sleep, but the amorous Carlyle was not to be put off, and kept after me. Finally, I became so irritated, I released a stream of very bad words at him, flounced into the bathroom, and slammed the door in his face.

He came after me, calling "Would you mind repeating that?" through the keyhole.

"Okay, I will." I opened the door, stared into his eyes and pronounced distinctly, "Ah . . . said . . . go . . . fuck . . . yourself!" What did I care, he was driving me crazy.

All of a sudden, I noticed he was not discouraged by my callous contempt, but very much aroused, desperate for me to say the words again.

He was so turned on, he pinned me to the bed and made passionate love to me, while I fixed my wandering gaze on the television and thought of Jon.

As I've said, Duke and his sporty friends were tickled over my starry-eyed attitude toward folks who, to them, were just the same as you and me. There were times when I would meet someone and just go crazy over them.

The foremost of my obsessions was the great Joe Di-Maggio, not only a fine sportsman, but above all, the husband of my lifelong idol, Marilyn Monroe.

Marilyn. This magnificent creature, who had struggled, suffered, and made it, was my inspiration, and from my teens I had nurtured a dream to follow in her star-studded footsteps. I had examined every facet of her tragic life, read every word written about her, and seen over and over every movie she'd made. I had drilled myself in her mannerisms and taught myself to imitate her voice down to the last breathy syllable.

In many ways, our lives really did parallel each other's. We had both been poverty-stricken orphans, had sustained sexual abuse and contempt from adults, and had determined early to slog it down the rocky road from the hollow to the glamorous life. As I developed physically, I was happy to realize even our shapes weren't dissimilar. Stranger still, our grandmothers had been the most important individuals in both our under-privileged lives, and ironically, their names were both Della. A chain of auspicious coincidences bound us to-gether, and it now appeared that Joe DiMaggio might be still another link.

Joe was friends with some of the regulars at Duke's, who knew how I felt about him, and when one evening someone handed me the phone and said Joe DiMaggio was on the other end, I decided to play along with the joke. "Hello, Joe, this is Elizabeth Ray speaking," I was using my Monroe voice, and I was astounded to recog-nize the real Joe DiMaggio's voice on the other end.

When I was in New York with Duke for a football game in November 1973, someone at a small pregame party said they were talking to Joe long-distance in San Francisco. Again, they put me on, and this time, I was bold enough to suggest he give me a call next time he was east.

A couple of weeks later, I was thrilled to hear from

him. Joe said he was arriving in New York on Sunday, December 1, to film a television commercial Monday, and invited me to brunch if I happened to be in New York that day. Naturally, I told him I was planning to be in New York that very Sunday, and would love to have brunch with him. Imagine, me dating the husband of the world's greatest sex symbol. What would those mean kids at Marshall High say if they could see me now?

I hardly slept the night before my date with Joe, and got up early to make sure my hair would be a soft cloud of fluffy platinum curls and that my makeup would be perfect.

My outfit was a red suede western-style suit and a white cotton blouse with cowboy pockets, very much like a costume I'd seen Marilyn wear in a picture. I looked terrific, but the weather didn't look nearly as good. Storm clouds had formed in the early morning, and by eleven, when I was supposed to catch the New York shuttle, a full scale blizzard was howling.

The airports were closed, and passengers returned to their homes as conditions became critical. Those with more compelling reasons to get to New York raced for the train, and I was among them.

I had intended to be in New York around noon, but it was now five o'clock and I had not called Joe for fear that he would suggest a postponement. Wild horses, hail, and brimstone could not have kept me away from New York that day.

At seven-thirty that evening, I battled my way out of Pennsylvania Station, almost bludgeoned a group of ladies for a cab, and was delivered, miraculously intact, to the New York Hilton. I ran straight to the lobby powder room and repaired my makeup, then walked to the house phones. To reach them, I had to pass a group of salesmen, driven inside by the foul weather, who were sitting around, shooting the breeze.

Making sure the ogle-eyed lotharios could hear me, I picked up the house phone and, in my best Monroe voice, announced, "Mr. DiMaggio's room, please." The salesmen nudged each other, but their amusement turned to shock when Joe came striding toward me across the lobby, told me I was even prettier than he'd expected, then whisked me off to dinner at La Scala, his favorite Italian restaurant. We fought our way through the blizzard to the restaurant a couple of blocks away and got snow in our hair and our eyes when the umbrella flipped inside out.

When we finally arrived at the warm, comfortable place, I was struck by the pictures of Joe and his late wife all over the room. I was overjoyed when the owner asked Joe if the young lady with him was an actress. Joe just smiled and squeezed my hand.

Joe is a quiet guy, who doesn't say much, but listens closely to others. I asked him things about himself, but he said they weren't exciting enough to talk about, and that he would rather find out all about me.

It was just a dream evening. Joe and I had a fabulous time together, and dated on and off whenever he was in the East. I became so fond of him that I carried the torch all the way to Hollywood, where I finally went in early 1975 to start my acting classes with Marilyn Monroe's revered teacher, Lee Strasberg.

Assuming Joe would be touched by my respect for

his dead wife's memory, I decided to duplicate her formula for achievement, and one of the first things I did in the movie capital was to arrange an appointment with photographer Tom Kelly the man who had taken Marilyn's immortal calendar picture.

My favorite role in acting class was the scene from *The Seven Year Itch,* when Marilyn Monroe arrives at her downstairs neighbor's with an unopened bottle of champagne.

Marilyn's bubbly opening lines were "Can I come in? I'm sorry I'm late," and she shows him her injured thumb, which she's hurt previously trying to open the champagne.

Finally, the day arrived when I had to perform the scene for the maestro himself. It turned out to be the same day as my appointment for pictures with Kelly, and to add to the confusion, the same day Joe was taking me to dinner. The coincidence was an omen, I told my girl friend Kathy who came with me to meet my Joe for a drink. And I was all too correct.

Joe wanted to watch something on television in his suite, so Kathy and I went up and messed around doing nothing much. Looking in the service refrigerator for something to drink, I found a bottle of champagne. I took it out, and fell into the role that was still very fresh on my mind. "I'm sorry I'm late," I purred.

"No problem," Joe said, distractedly turning on the set before walking into the bathroom. "Can I come in?" I asked coyly.

"You certainly cannot," he yelled through the closed door. "I'll be out in a moment."

When he came out, he settled himself in the easy

chair, and proceeded to become transfixed by the game on television.

I made one more gallant attempt to get him to acknowledge my finest role. Mincing over toward him, I held out a nastily reddened finger and the champagne bottle with the supposedly stubborn cork still intact. "Oh, just look at my thumb," I pouted. The accent was letter perfect. "I've been trying to get this open for hours. Can you help me?"

"Give it here," he said absentmindedly. And, without taking his eyes off the set, he whistled, "My God, Elizabeth, will you look at that home run!"

This was a romantic evening with the husband of the world's goddess of sex? Well, I thought, so long to you, Joe DiMaggio!

12
Red, White—and Blue

Each Fourth of July, because it represented independence, I would sit down to analyze my progress and to evaluate my future. For my first several Fourths in Washington, I had been pleased with my achievements as the glamorous playmate of the men who ran America.

My black book was full of the private numbers of public figures, I had a nice apartment, an expensive sportscar, and, considering my lack of education, I had an enviable job.

It gave me a tremendous feeling of belonging when important people accepted me into their company, and I would often lie awake nights thinking how lucky I was. I could easily have been slinging hash in the S and W diner in Asheville, yet here I was among the famous and the powerful, and I could hardly believe my good fortune.

My important dates always told me how beautiful I was. They thought of me as a soft, sexy girl, not as a whore, and I never gave them any hassle—with the exception of one Congressman who really deserved it.

While I was still dating him, this particular legislator had the bad manners to ask me to fix him up with my good-looking girl friend, Valentina. I was very insulted and decided he needed to be taught a lesson.

One night, as we were dining together at Gusti's, he brought up the subject again. "When am I going to get together with Valentina?" he asked hornily.

"If that's what you really want," I said sweetly, "I'll fix you up right away."

"You will?" He was like a cat hot on the tail of a canary.

I got up and went to the pay booth, dialed, and when the party answered, said, "Hold on, please, for long-distance."

Meantime, the Congressman had left the table and followed me to the booth. "Here," I handed him the phone, with my hand across the mouthpiece. "If you insist, please go ahead and make out with Valentina."

He grabbed the phone from me and roared into the mouthpiece, "Hi, Valentina, baby. I'm with Elizabeth over at Gusti's, and we're having a swinging time. Why don't you come over and join us?"

He didn't pause to see whom I had on the other end. If he had, he would have known it was not Valentina, but his own wife. Before he finished his speech, I had walked back to the table, picked up my coat, and got the hell out of there. So much for the wayward representative, whose wings had just sustained a radical clip job.

As the years in Washington went by, I had to do more and more kinky sex in order to keep myself going. My dental and medical bills were collected in trade, and I could walk into the top restaurant in every major city in America and eat free, but I was paying dearly for the privileges.

In 1973 I bought a much too expensive mink coat which I put on American Express. I wasn't allowed to pay it off in installments, and in a couple of months, they were threatening to put my account into the delinquent file.

I called American Express, begging for time to pay, and, luckily, got a man who was understanding. He asked how on earth did I get myself into such a tight financial bind, and I told him I was a model, but that a big job had just fallen through. To prove my occupation, I sent him a nude picture, and the following week he was calling me to say that I had a fantastic body, that I could pay the bill in installments, and that he would love to meet me.

With the grocery clerk from the A&P, it was only a slightly different story. When I promised to pay him for the twenty-three-dollar check I bounced, he suggested I ask him over for a drink. However, when a drink was all I offered him, he became very nasty and demanded the cash immediately.

Gradually, I was becoming bored to death with sitting around all day, staring at the filing cabinets then going straight home at night to wait for my boss to decide if he had time to screw me.

Battle was taking up more and more of my time. In a way, his possessiveness was a compliment, but he also had a mistress who got to go on the European junkets with him, while I was expected to languish at home for a mere $12,000. If only I had had a career to fall back on, I would have dumped him instantly, but I was trapped.

Luckily, Battle continued to leave Washington on Thursday evening and return on Monday morning, which still left me three days a week to play, although it was a far cry from the freedom I was used to.

Finally, I heard a Senator was looking for a part-time receptionist and I decided to apply. Part-time work would afford the perfect opportunity to study drama and earn a living at the same time, and I even had legitimate reception experience on the Hill.

The Senator asked me to come by for an interview, indicated I had an excellent chance at the job, and told me to call him to confirm it the next day. Two hours after our conversation, I received a call from his close friend, the chairman of a huge southern industrial concern, who was visiting Washington on business.

This man told me the Senator had given him my name, then proceeded to invite me to dinner that night. I declined because I already had a date, and the next morning when I called to see if I had the job, the Senator stalled and told me to call him some other time.

Now it was July 4, 1974, and I was sitting in the tub thinking about my future, and the whole depressing puzzle was beginning to come together. I didn't have a boyfriend I cared about because I had been too busy chasing celebrities, and even if I did love someone, he wouldn't put up with my obligations to Senator Battle. I had painted myself into a corner and if I never again saw another cock, I would be perfectly happy.

After a good, cleansing cry, I decided to find me a psychiatrist who would get me out of this mess and into a more fulfilling way of life, but the first shrink I tried, only wanted to talk about sex.

"It's not that I want sex," I told him. "I have plenty of that already," but he kept pressing the point.

"Look, sex is not my problem," I insisted. "I want someone I can love, relate to, and call my own. Plus, I'm having a lot of hassle at work."

The shrink knew I had a lot of experience with married men, so he started talking about hypothetical situations, which didn't relate to me at all.

"If you were in love with a married man with three children," he asked me, "would you expect him to leave his wife?"

"I've never even wanted anyone to leave a spouse," I asserted. "That's not my scene at all. I'm concerned only about my job, and about finding someone to fall in love with."

He brushed that aside. "Well, if you came across a problem like the one I ve described, how would you handle it? What would you do?"

"I don't think you're referring to me at all," I insisted, so he started telling me that during the summer when his wife was away, he had been cruising the bars and met, and fallen in love with a married woman. All of a sudden, I was supposed to be *his* psychiatrist.

"Listen," I said, "don't assume I can help you when I need advice myself."

He laughed about that, then suggested I lie down on the sofa and relax, which I did, because I knew it was okay to do so in a shrink's office without any fears.

The doctor put a blanket over me and told me to close my eyes. I felt anxious. "What are you doing now?"

"You're going to feel much better," he said, smiling benevolently, "because I'm going to hypnotize you."

"Oh no, you're not," I said, jumping off the couch and diving for the door, but this nutcase was blocking my path. He wouldn't let me by, so I screamed as loud as I could just as his next patient happened to walk in. As I bolted out of that office, I yelled back at him that he really needed to see a good psychiatrist.

My second doctor, thank God, helped me a great deal. He was able to demonstrate how I'd been lurching through life, thinking the world owed me something, because of my mistaken belief that everyone else already had it handed to them on a silver platter. He explained why I always teetered on the edge of the cliff in my relentless pursuit of acceptance, how these VIPs with their herd instincts were really "circle jerkers" who could open or close the hands for one more or less cavort without a shrug, and how this celebrity worship had become really too much to handle. Above all, he showed me why my achievements ultimately felt hollow.

We worked on my problem, which the doctor referred to as "pan-seductiveness." It was this condition that caused me to exercise my compulsive need to be noticed by going to bed with men, and to trade-up in my conquests. Unfortunately, none of this gave me the affection I craved.

I told the psychiatrist that whenever I was blue, I would cry over my mother, blaming everything on her, always regretting the fact I'd never really been loved by her.

I had last seen Robbie some twenty years earlier, and I began to think how terrible it would be if anything happened to either of us and we never got to know what the other one was about.

I had also resolved to make my break from Washington and enroll in acting school with Lee Strasberg, Marilyn Monroe's illustrious teacher. His school was in Los Angeles, and I was scheduled to begin early in 1975, but before I left, I wanted to see my mother. It was important for her to know how far I had come with my influential political friends and to tell the folks back home about my beautiful apartment and expensive sportscar. Even now, it was important that she be proud of me. I wanted to look at her and forgive her in my heart.

In order even to communicate with Robbie, who lived in a remote part of the Carolina hills, I had to have a telephone installed in her house. As soon as that was done, I called her and said I was going to send her a ticket to come and visit me in Washington. At first she was afraid, never having left Carolina since our disastrous Detroit trip, let alone flown in a plane.

Eventually, she agreed to make this odyssey the week prior to Thanksgiving, 1974. On the day she was supposed to arrive, I took off from work and arrived at the airport half an hour early to meet her.

The plane was supposed to arrive at four o'clock, and

I checked everyone who came off the plane, not sure if I would recognize her.

When there definitely was no Robbie on the flight, I became very worried and called my aunt in Asheville. She said my mother had left early that morning, so I called my answering service, but they had no message from her. I checked every flight for the next hour, feeling guilty because I had prevailed on her to come to Washington in the first place. If anything terrible happened to her now, it would be my fault.

By five o'clock, I was ready to go to the police station when I heard Miss Betty Lou Ray being paged over the loudspeaker.

As I came upon a middle-aged woman who was definitely an older Robbie, I tried to hold back tears of relief mixed with anger. I simply couldn't be nasty to her after so many years, so after a quick, awkward embrace, I pleasantly asked her what had happened.

"Well, Betty," she said, "I got to talking to a man on the plane, and I walked over here with him while he bought himself a hot dog." The man drifted off, but not before Robbie got a phone number out of him. She definitely wouldn't have passed for a Washington matron.

Next morning, she expressed interest in seeing the famous Capitol, and I promised we'd go if, in exchange, she would agree to take a bath and clean herself up. Afterward, I fixed her makeup and bought her a nice burgundy corduroy pants-suit, a sweater, a coat, handbag, shoes, and underwear as well. Next, I took her to the Hill beauty shop to have her hair fixed, and when she was all decked out, she really looked good.

Since I assumed Robbie was oblivious to politics, I was surprised when she asked if she could meet her Congressman, Roy M. Taylor.

Well, I thought, she looks good, and I shouldn't be ashamed of her. I was proud that I knew Congressman Taylor and could personally ask him to meet my mother.

"I'll arrange for you to meet Congressman Taylor," I said, "but there's one thing I must ask you to do before you see him."

"What's that, Betty Lou?" she drawled.

"You will have to spit out your chewing tobacco." To make sure she wasn't overcome by sudden uncontrollable urges, I confiscated her supply and hid it from her.

Congressman Taylor was very charming and friendly, and we all posed for pictures together on the steps of the Capitol with the big dome behind us.

Next evening, Robbie, looking very attractive in her new image, handed me a crumpled piece of scrap paper with the telephone number of the man she had met on the plane, and asked me to invite him over for coffee. I did ask him, but he never came, and Robbie was despondent.

To get her mind off her troubles, I called a friend who worked in the Immigration and Naturalization Service and had him take us out to dinner. I was apprehensive at first about introducing my mother, but she was very sweet and enjoyable. She even started flirting with the Chinese waiter, kidding him about wanting to get his phone number. "Don't worry," I tried to convince her, "I'll get it for you later."

Robbie seemed to be having the time of her life, but

after a few days, she got very homesick and wanted to leave, and I didn't try to stop her. Before she got back on the plane, she assured me she had always loved me in her fashion, and always would, and I told her it was mutual.

Once she was gone I missed her, but not for long. A week later, I received a call from Congressman Taylor, who sounded slightly put out. That very morning he had received a clipping in the mail from the *Marshall News-Record,* featuring a picture of him standing on the Capitol steps with none other than my mother, beaming alongside him. Good old Robbie still hadn't given up, and I'd inherited her perseverance, which would stand me in good stead when I hit Hollywood.

At the time, I was still working for Senator Battle, but was preparing to leave for California within the month. When I mustered the courage to tell him I was going, he was quite annoyed and informed me that once I went, I needn't bother coming back.

"That's fine with me," I said, "because next time you see me, you'll be asking for my autograph."

As a last resort, he asked me to reconsider, and, for a moment, I felt that there may have been some real sentiment deep down in his Yankee heart. Never a man to leave you feeling good, Senator Battle's parting words were brief and to the point: "Don't forget to leave me your girl friend's number."

13
Hollywood and Bust

Hollywood exceeded my wildest expectations, and that was really saying something. Within a week of arriving, I was quietly dining with a handsome Beverly Hills lawyer in the back parlor of a barbeque restaurant when we heard a sharp volley of reports like a car backfiring.

My date ran to the front parlor to investigate, and in a moment, was calling to me in panic, "Let's get the hell out of this place!"

Without stopping to grab the lovely red suede jacket I'd worn on my first date with Joe DiMaggio, I headed straight through the side door and kept running till I caught up with my gallant escort almost a block away.

"What happened in the other room?" I gasped.

"There was a woman lying bleeding on the floor," he said, his face still ashen. "And a big guy with a horrible face was standing over her with a pistol in his hand."

Next morning, when I read about the murder in the

Los Angeles Times, I said to myself I always knew this was going to be a wild old town, but I hadn't realized just how wild. Chills aside, there were plenty of thrills to be had in Hollywood. Those legendary wide-screen figures actually did exist, as I discovered on my very first night in Los Angeles. While making a telephone call in the lobby of the Beverly Wilshire Hotel, I could not hide my amazement at seeing a famous person standing alongside me. "My God," I said, half to myself, "is that John Wayne?"

"Yep," he grinned, amused, "it's me."

Everything about Hollywood was very exciting to me. I loved buzzing along streets with names I'd read about in fan magazines and racing down Sunset Boulevard with the top down and the radio playing. I had to keep pinching myself and saying, "This is it, you're really here!"

Since I've always preferred the casual look, I adapted very easily to the local life-style and began dressing in expensive jeans and bare halter tops. Such a costume flattered me, as did my new tan, and I got lots of attention everywhere I went.

I realized very quickly that in order to get anywhere in Los Angeles, you have to be in the right clique, but in order to get into the right clique, you have to be someone. In other words, everyone is so obsessed with success that people who've already made it don't want to be bothered with people who haven't, and the latter don't want to be hamstrung by anyone who can't help them move ahead.

Another thing that surprised me was the lack of dinner invitations. In Washington, a date would at least wine and dine you before asking for the obvious. In L.A., you settled for a hamburger or nothing at all. Everyone seemed short of cash and between jobs, obsessed only with meeting the payments on their new Rolls Royce.

There was a lot of ego-tripping going on, with everyone watching their own movies on closed-circuit television or having themselves paged in the celebrity-studded Polo Lounge of the Beverly Hills Hotel.

It was necessary to be represented by an agent if you wanted to get anywhere in movies, but you couldn't get an agent unless you were somewhere already. Fortunately, I overcame this handicap through my valuable Washington contact, Jack Valenti, president of the Motion Picture Association, whom I saw one evening in the Polo Lounge.

With my customary lack of restraint, I ran over and reintroduced myself, "Hi, I'm Liz Ray. Remember me?"

He was gracious enough to say he absolutely did, and presented me to the man sitting with him, the agent Bud Maas. "You're just the person I wanted to meet," I bubbled, then convinced him to take me on as a client.

What really delighted me about the so-called glamour capital of the world was learning that Hollywood actually looked up to Washington. Whenever I went on job interviews, I would be asked, "Why would you leave a place with all that power and excitement to come out here?" In Los Angeles, people talked about politicians as though they were gods, and everyone was tremendously impressed that I personally knew all those congressmen and senators.

Even without my Washington credits, however, I would have fitted right into the Los Angeles scene, because it is almost identical to Miami, Washington, and New York. In seeking out the powerful, I found myself in the same experiences, sometimes with the same cast of characters, as I had had in Washington.

I was dating one famous married man, who made sure he kept me way in the background. Although he was invited to attend the 1975 Academy Awards ceremonies, he slipped away early to have a candlelight dinner with me.

Another famous date, a big name noted for his G-rated image, once called me at Strasberg's to ask if I'd seen my gynecologist recently. I thought it was a peculiar question, but I told him I'd had a thorough checkup at Johns Hopkins before I left Washington.

"I mean, in the last couple of weeks?" he persisted.

When I asked him why he was so concerned, he hesitated a moment, then broke the good news. "Because I've come down with something sinister, and I think you're involved."

I didn't even replace the phone on the hook before jumping in my car and racing over to the emergency ward of U.C.L.A. hospital. I had always taken pains to be super-clean, and I was embarrassed to tears that I had passed some awful illness on to such an important man. I ran to the emergency desk and whispered my problem to the duty nurse.

"Speak up," she said loudly. "I can't hear you."

I was too ashamed to repeat the words, so I wrote it all down on a piece of paper and gave it to her.

"VD?" she bellowed. "What's wrong with that, girl? We have dozens of women in here every day with the same problem."

But those dozens of women hadn't given a social disease to one of America's best-loved stars, I thought, as she led me into an examing room to be tested.

I was still very upset when I went home, and, seeking sympathy, I called a girl friend in New York and spilled the whole terrible story. Her reaction was that I should ask the famous Mr. Wholesome to check with his other female friends and get himself tested. Men, she lectured me, always get away with blaming the woman, who automatically assume it's their fault.

My friend was right, as I found out when I collected my clean bill of health from the hospital. I immediately mailed off the "negative" certificate as positive proof to Mr. Wholesome.

Realizing I was heading down the primrose path to trouble, I vowed not to let myself make the same mistake again. Socializing and scooting around L.A. meant taking more risks than in Washington, and, besides, I had come to Hollywood to pursue a serious career. I immediately tone down my extracurricular activities to devote myself to more serious endeavors.

On the couple of occasions when I did go to parties, I was really turned off to the tarnish I saw on the glitter of Tinseltown. At one affair, given for a visiting Washington judge at a producer's house, drugs were passed instead of drinks, and the real purpose of the party, it soon became clear, was to get some kind of a scene going. That was a bitter disappointment, but it couldn't touch my subsequent disillusionment when I discovered my favorite bachelor movie idol was just some guy who was into orgies.

I went along to this stylish gathering as the guest of a rich girl friend, and soon after I arrived, I was thrilled to be introduced to this really big, really handsome star. This great-looking, rough-talking, all-male man, whom I'll call Sonny, asked me first what I did, then who I was.

I told him, honestly, that I was trying to be an actress, and he said, "Well, you should try to get yourself a nude spread in *Playboy* first."

"How do I do that?" I asked eagerly.

"Well," he replied, grinning that famous bad-boy grin, "I've got connections there, but we've got to check you out first."

"What do you mean?" I was more than a little baffled.

"Well, I mean I want to know if your tits are real," he said, not bothering to beat around the bush. "Or are they fake?"

"They're real," I said, getting a little turned off to his brusque manner.

"Well, I don't believe you, but I'm willing to let you prove it if you want," he announced sternly.

"How?" I was planning to have my agent send him one of Tom Kelly's beautiful nude photos of me.

"Why don't you take off your top?" he suggested in a very businesslike manner.

There were a half a dozen guys and girls sitting around, and my girl friend, Sally, was already involved in a game of backgammon with another guest.

"I'd prefer not to," I murmured.

"If you don't want to remove it," he urged, "let one of us guys do it for you." He was assuming his usual cocky air and gave the other guys a knowing look.

"No way," I said firmly. "Not a chance."

"Well, if you won't let the boys undress you, how about letting Jane do it? She hasn't taken her eyes off you since you walked in." I looked over at the girl named Jane, who was parting her lips and beckoning me with her tongue.

Sally looked up from backgammon, and when our eyes met, we instinctively decided this scene was too steep for us. We got up and left, but not before I walked casually past the big star and cooly suggested he take some of the padding out of his crotch.

Despite my extracurricular ups and downs, school was terrific, and I enjoyed the feeling that I was having something like a college experience. We were located in Hollywood, which had grown a little seedy since its golden days, but which was still full of famous names like the Brown Derby, and streets like Hollywood and Vine. For the first time in my life, I was working very hard. My studies were going fine, and I was moving toward a level at which I would be eligible to study in a group conducted by Lee Strasberg himself.

Despite my serious efforts to develop my ability, I was worried that I might not make the the grade. I needed some counseling, I decided, and arranged for a private appointment after class with one of the instructors. He led me into his office, closed the door, asked me to tell him my problems and listened sympathetically while I poured out my fears. ·

"But that's all in your mind," he urged me. "You have a very good chance of moving up."

"What makes you say that?" I was desperate for re-assurance.

"Because I know everyone in the business," he smiled, "and I can introduce you to all the right people."

"But what good is that if I don't have ability, or experience, or if I freeze up in an audition?"

"Well, you definitely do have talent," my instructor reiterated.

"I do? That's wonderful!" I was practically jumping up and down with joy.

"Sure, and you can really turn people on," he murmured, inching closer. "Just look what you're doing to me."

I found myself looking down on this huge erection. Before my eyes, he speedily unzipped, took out his cock, and told me to suck him off. No matter which way or where you go about things, the legitimate job is always second to the blow job. I knew there was no use fighting that, so, under the circumstances, I gave him what he wanted, and it served me well, since the teacher always gave me special attention after that night.

As I tenaciously pursued my career by doing the rounds of interviews, I got all kinds of propositions. The typical question after I go through the door was "Do you object to nudity?"

My answer was always yes, because I was no longer going to settle for being a body and a pair of boobs.

"Well, you're not what we're looking for," they'd always say, and I'd move on.

At one major studio, I was asked by the producer's associates to take care of the big man's physical as well as artistic needs. "Listen," one of the henchmen said as I was about to go in, "poor guy just had a lousy lunch, and he feels bad. Try to cheer him up, know what I mean?"

I certainly did know. It was the old Pudgy Contractor–Nicky the Turk treatment, and I dreaded doing it, but I had no choice. How could I risk passing up the chance for a real part in a major movie?

In I went to the plush inner office, where the producer handed me a script, but when I asked him if I could do my own scene from *The Seven Year Itch* instead, he didn't object.

And when I requested a champagne bottle to use as a prop, I was given a magnum of Moet Chandon from a refrigerator in the bar. I was really flattered that such a famous producer was so anxious to please me and make me feel relaxed.

I launched into my act, brandishing the champagne and two glasses, but when I came to the part where the bottle had to be opened, I paused.

"You don't really need it opened, do you?" The producer was pleading with me to say no.

"Oh, I definitely do," I whispered in character. "It wouldn't be the same performance if we left it sealed."

The word *performance* seemed to change his mind, and somewhat reluctantly he opened the big bottle of expensive champagne. I took only two sips from my glass, because I really don't drink, then put it aside, and went on with the scene.

"W-wait a minute," the producer interrupted. "When's the part where you take off your clothes?"

"That's further on," I teased him, sashaying to the sofa and sitting down. He joined me, and started trying to get romantic. As I removed his hands from my thighs and shoulders, I cautioned him, "Wait a while, please."

When I came to the part where I say, "Well, I really have to be going now," he intensified his attack, assuming that we were approaching the good part.

"Hold off," I told him, walking from the room while he waited, horny as anything, expecting me to return naked. Instead, I just kept walking until I reached my car, jumped in, and drove on home, leaving him with an enormous bottle of champagne and a hard-on to match.

There were many such incidents, but for the first few months, they didn't make a dent in my dreams, for I vowed to beat the system yet. It looked like I'd finally succeeded when another producer offered me the part of a sexy cigarette girl who captures the fancy of a Howard Hughes–type lover. This role was really up my alley, and I could even cite my actual experience as a cigarette girl.

The producer had taken me out to lunch a couple of times, and I got the strong impression that he would have liked an invitation back to my place, but I always made excuses about being late for class.

After a couple of weeks of cheap hamburger-lunches, the movie role seemed more and more remote, and one day, as we were sitting outside my apartment building, I asked him outright when were we going to sign the contract.

"Well," he equivocated, "I was wondering. I'm going to give you this coveted role, but what are you going to do for me in return?"

"What do you mean?" I just stared at him.

"I don't know if you realize it," he said, "but I have at least twenty girls a week after this part, and all of them ask what they can do for me."

"Well, just tell me exactly what it is you want."

"I want you to ask me upstairs to your place and to have intercourse with me," he said boldly.

"I'm not interested in sex," I responded.

"You don't look as if you're not interested," he grinned. "You're a very sexy girl."

"Well, I don't have intercourse with people I don't know," I declared righteously.

"In that case," he suggested, "how do you feel about giving head?"

I'd worked harder, longer, and straighter for a Hollywood career than for anything else I'd ever undertaken. I had credentials, contacts, and drive, yet all I saw in the six months in Hollywood was a lot of promising and propositioning by people who were too much on the make to help anyone else out. After thier lust cooled, they would go back on their word.

In Washington, people always kept their word, about helpful introductions, an airline reservation, and job opportunities. In L.A., no one did anything they said they would. I began to see that the real power was back in Washington, not in Hollywood, and in Washington I was an accepted member of the club.

I began to feel hopeless about succeeding in Hollywood, because everywhere you turned, there were dozens of beautiful girls, all settling for sales positions and waitressing jobs. It was not so much a matter of connections as a question of blind luck. I could make out that very day, or spend the next ten years waiting for a break that never came.

Now, after a dozen producers had already strung me along, my latest prospect was interested only in a blow job, without any guarantees attached. I was really pissed off.

Without even giving this guy an insulting answer, I stepped out of his car, flung open the door, ran up to my apartment, threw some clothes into a suitcase, and without looking over my shoulder headed for the airport.

By the next day, I was back home in our nation's capital. It was fantastic to see that beautiful city again, and the first thing I did, of course, was to call up Senator Battle. Only after a six-month separation did I realize how much, despite our odd relationship, we had grown on each other, even if neither of us would admit it. "Hi," I said, "it's me. I'm in town."

"What the hell are you doing here?" he grumbled.

"Just visiting," I answered coyly.

"Good, because, if you're looking for a job again, you're out of luck." He sounded as if he had grown even nastier during our time apart. "Why the hell did you leave in the first place? I told you you'd be back."

Before I could say anything provocative, he cut me short to go to the House floor to vote. When I asked him to call me back later, he advised me not to hold my breath.

Meanwhile, I myself went over to the House floor to

say hello to all my Congressional friends, who were thrilled to see me. One eastern Congressman, whom I'd never met before, introduced himself and asked who I was and what I was doing there.

"I'm looking for an apartment and a job," I found myself saying.

"I think I can help you out," he said, leading me to the Speaker's office, where he called the superintendent of an apartment building he owned. In seconds, I had a place to live. The helpful Congressman now led me toward an alcove alongside the Capitol steps, and whispered, "How discreet are you?"

"Very, otherwise I wouldn't be here."

"Well," he said, resting his briefcase against a pillar, "I want you to see what you are doing to me."

Of course, he had a huge erection and was about to ask for a date when none other than Senator Battle came striding by.

"There's my ex-boss," I said, pointing to the feared and powerful man. "I've got to go."

The Congressman from the East didn't take a second, but hurried off precisely as Battle arrived.

"Hello, sir," I said. "It's really good to see you," and I meant it.

"Hrrmph" was all he mumbled, and then, "what are you doing for dinner tonight?"

Epilogue
The State of the Union

Since I've come back to the bosom of our nation, life's been pretty fine. I'm now the proud occupant of a big, beautiful office, complete with giant couch, a lock on the door, and my own private hotline. You'd hardly know it was an office at all, except for the baby blue electric typewriter, placed prettily on an imitation Chippendale table near the eighteenth-century desk.

My office is the perfect setting for intimate, late afternoon gatherings or for champagne-and-sympathy sessions with Senator Battle. During my boss's recent personal problems, he often sought solace on my couch, and it was from there that he broke the news about my promotion.

To my surprise, he announced that as soon as Congress adjourned, he was going to marry that girl he always took to Europe. "She was Mistress Number One, and you've been Mistress Number Two," he explained. "But now I'm giving you a big promotion, and, effective my wedding day, you're going to be Mistress Number One!"

My feelings about his move were very mixed, and I was about to throw a scene when Battle tossed in the bonus. Afraid I was suffering the strains of overwork, my considerate employer was treating me to an all-expenses-paid junket on a lush Caribbean island, and although I never went I later found out that it had the most primitive telephone system in the Western Hemisphere. By a strange coincidence, I would have left four days before the Senator's wedding and returned the evening before he got back from his European honeymoon.

I was tempted to laugh out loud, until I realized that the mistress arrangement would suit both of us perfectly. He'd go on enjoying my favors, and I'd continue enjoying his. Once again, Battle had wheeled and dealed the perfect political solution.

As I looked deep into the eyes of the most terrifying man in Washington, I knew at last why he meant so much to me. Senator Otis Battle was everything I loved about the Washington scene, all the power, the excitement, "the juice" that drew me from a Carolina shack to the corridors of Congress. Well I, for one, was glad to be there, and reaching for his zipper, I said in my best Marilyn voice, "I've been trying to get this open for hours. Can you help me?"

THE GARGOYLE CONSPIRACY

A novel by
Marvin H. Albert

A bomb explodes in the Rome airport, leaving shreds of human flesh strewn about the wreckage. But it was nothing compared to what was to come. It was only the first step of a master terrorist who combined irresistible sexual seduction, all-powerful Arab oil money, an army of terrorist assassins and the latest in sophisticated weaponry in a plot to assassinate the American Secretary of State.

A great new thriller guaranteed to hold you on excitement's edge from the first explosive page to the ultimate shattering shock.

A Dell Book $1.95   (5239-02)

The jaws of horror were closing on her again-- and this time there was no escape!

Where Are The Children?

by Mary H. Clark

Nancy Harmon had fled the evil of her first marriage, the macabre deaths of her two little children, the hideous charges that had been made against her. She changed her name, dyed her hair, moved from California to New England. Now married again, she had two lovely new children and a happiness-filled life . . . until the morning when she looked for her children and found only one tattered red mitten and knew that the nightmare was beginning again.

"Absolutely riveting horror!" —*Publishers Weekly*

"An extravagantly plotted page-turner. It will make you hold your breath!" —*Kirkus Reviews*

A DELL BOOK $1.95
(9593-04)

The sensational new life-saving diet
discovery that tells you that you are
not eating enough!

Dr. Siegal's Natural Fiber Permanent Weight-Loss Diet

by Sanford Siegal, D.O., M.D.

If you are an ordinary American, you are probably
spending more and more for food, consuming more
and more calories, gaining more and more weight,
being threatened by more and more diseases—yet you
are really eating less and less.

Now a leading diet doctor shows you how to
spend less, consume fewer calories, lose weight and
decrease your chances of premature death—all by
eating more.

Try it. You'll love what it does to your mealtime
pleasure. And you'll adore what it does for you.